Explanation

M.A.B. Institutions are shewn in Black·

▰ Hospitals		✚ Ambulance Stations.	
▰ Wharves		● Other Institutions.	
⊕ Remand Homes		--- Underground	
▥ Homes for Defective children		-·- County Boundary.	
✚ Ringworm Schools		—— Railways	
▯ Ophthalmic Schools		⊟⊟⊟ Main Roads	

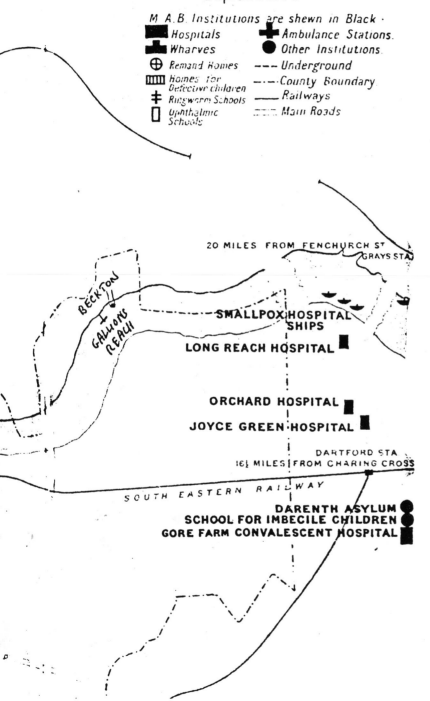

20 MILES FROM FENCHURCH ST
GRAYS STA

BECKTON

GALLIONS REACH

SMALLPOX HOSPITAL SHIPS

LONG REACH HOSPITAL

ORCHARD HOSPITAL

JOYCE GREEN HOSPITAL

DARTFORD STA
16½ MILES FROM CHARING CROSS

SOUTH EASTERN RAILWAY

DARENTH ASYLUM
SCHOOL FOR IMBECILE CHILDREN
GORE FARM CONVALESCENT HOSPITAL

Dartford's Capital River 1989
has been published
in a Limited Edition
of which this is

Number 404

A list of original subscribers
is printed at
the back of the book.

DARTFORD'S CAPITAL RIVER

FRONT COVER: A stumpy spritsail barge with topsail glides past the
hospital ships, with Beacon Hill, Purfleet in the background.

Smallpox hospital ships *Atlas, Endymion* and *Castalia* at Long Reach.

DARTFORD'S CAPITAL RIVER

Paddle Steamers, Personalities and Smallpox Boats

BY

JOHN BURNE

BARRACUDA BOOKS LIMITED
BUCKINGHAM, ENGLAND
MCMLXXXIX

PUBLISHED BY BARRACUDA BOOKS LIMITED
BUCKINGHAM, ENGLAND
AND PRINTED BY
MACDERMOTT & CHANT LIMITED
ENGLAND & WALES

BOUND BY
WBC BOOKBINDERS LIMITED
MAESTEG, WALES

JACKET PRINTED BY
CHENEY & SONS LIMITED
BANBURY, OXON

LITHOGRAPHY BY
CAMERA-GRAPHIC LIMITED
AMERSHAM, ENGLAND

DISPLAY SET IN BASKERVILLE
AND TEXT SET IN 10½/12pt BASKERVILLE BY
KEY COMPOSITION
NORTHAMPTON, ENGLAND

ISBN 0 86023 454 1

CONTENTS

Acknowledgements

My thanks to the Dartford Health Authority for permission to delve into the River Hospitals records, and to Dr Haas Patel for the use of the facilities of the Postgraduate Centre, Joyce Green Hospital. Tania Bourne and Sue Franklin did much of the typing, and Ian and Andrew Smith formatted me and my computer to work in harmony and so eased the burden of indexing; to these four much thanks.

Ken Jarvis and his staff at Dartford Public Library gave invaluable support in many ways and the following provided key information or help in their own fields: Edwin Shearing (canal history), John Cassell (Thames barges), Geoff Burchell (photography), Mr D.J. Lyon (National Maritime Museum), Dr Spence Galbraith (old MAB/LCC records), John A. Tyler (Joyce Green Airfield), Sheila Blackman (Dartford family histories), Mr Vaughan (Greenhithe historian) and the many members of the hospitals staff, past and present, who have fed me with valuable snippets of information.

To my family I owe a special debt; to my forebears who, by their writings over 100 years, have stimulated in me the historical yen, and to the present generations for their support, especially my wife, Winifred, and my daughter, Helen Hicks who has diligently read the manuscript and made many valuable suggestions. I hope I have not failed them.

Finally my grateful admiration to the men and women who over the last 100 or so years lived, and sometimes died, in the bizarre circumstances that made Long Reach a place apart. They and their doings deserve to be remembered and this I have attempted.

Glossary

THE METROPOLITAN ASYLUMS BOARD (MAB) 1867. Set up to administer the Metropolitan Asylums District (MAD) for the reception and relief of London rate-aided poor, suffering from smallpox, fever or insanity. It consisted of the Parishes & Poor Law Unions of the Metropolis.

BOARDS OF GUARDIANS (of the Poor). The bodies who administered the workhouses of the Poor Law Unions & Parishes. In the Metropolis there were about 30, half of them being Unions and half Parishes. Each sent one or more representative to the MAB.

ORSETT UNION. An Essex Poor Law Union (PLU) which included Purfleet. It was formed, like Dartford PLU, by Act of Parliament 1834.

LOCAL GOVERNMENT BOARD (LGB) 1871. Formed by merger of three government departments including Poor Law Board. Forerunner of Ministry of Health, 1919.

ERITH LOCAL BOARD (ELB). Second tier local health authority under overall control of the LGB. Western boundary formed by Woolwich, which was in the MAD.

LONDON COUNTY COUNCIL (LCC). 1889. Swallowed MAB Hospitals April 1930, to add to their own chain. Hospitals transferred to NHS 1948.

EMERGENCY MEDICAL SERVICE (EMS) 1939–1945. Run by Ministry of Health (MOH), successor to LGB.

REGISTERED FEVER NURSE (RFN). 1919 Nurses Registration Act. Before then the MAB had their own training scheme and certificates.

RIVER HOSPITALS. The group of hospitals built by the MAB to replace the Smallpox Ships (Floating Hospital). They were Long Reach & Orchard (temporary) and Joyce Green (permanent) Hospitals.

LDDC. London Docks Development Corporation.

RAMC. Royal Army Medical Corps.

FOREWORD

by the Rt Hon the Lord Irving of Dartford DL

In 1952 I became a member of the Dartford Borough Council, which regularly received reports on the public health from its Medical Officer of Health. Often these were dramatic, as on the occasion when Dr Hudson needed to transport a lead coffin containing the remains of a smallpox victim through the town, and, not being able to find a driver for the van, had to do the job himself.

In 1955, when I became the Member of Parliament for Dartford, I became even more aware of the public concern at reading in the national press that a smallpox case had been discovered and removed to Dartford.

I always marvelled at the devotion of the nursing staff who, when a case arrived, were confined in isolation with the patient until either his death or recovery.

In 1972 I was asked to be Chairman of Dartford and Darenth Hospital Management Committee, which was a new group bringing nearly a dozen hospitals together, including Joyce Green. This brought me even more directly into contact with the remarkable history and achievements of the river hospitals.

I visited several times the Long Reach Tavern, one of the most unusual pubs I have ever been in, and I was sorry when it was demolished.

I have always hoped that someone would undertake the work of writing a history of the river and its hospitals as I too had been aware of the fascinating history of the area, the marshes and the river.

I cannot think of anyone more suited to do this work than Dr Burne, with his long and distinguished service to these hospitals. I congratulate him on a splendid effort which I am sure will appeal to many people.

Coat of Arms of the MAB with motto 'I learn to succour the wretched'.

ABOVE: View towards Erith from the deck of the *Atlas*. CENTRE: Stereo view of Long Reach, c1900. Sheep graze, oblivious of flood risk, Tavern on the horizon. BELOW: The same view in 1988: new flood barrier in Dartford Creek and man-made mound on the horizon. (A)

LONG REACH

'Where shall I begin please your Majesty? the White Rabbit asked.
Begin at the beginning, the King said very gravely
and go on till you come to the end: then stop.'
Alice in Wonderland, Lewis Carroll

The southern shore of Long Reach with its extensive marshes looks more like Essex than Kent; yet, for all its treeless peaty isolation, it has been much used over the years. This may have started when the first boat crossed from Purfleet centuries ago, before the first low embankment provided some protection from the seasonal tidal flooding. Little wonder they were called saltmarshes and not rated highly as agricultural land.

Trade must have been boosted when the pilgrims from East Anglia came down the Mermaids Causeway, across the Aveley marshes on their way to Canterbury, not forgetting to refresh themselves at any well placed hostel; history does not disclose when the first tavern came to Long Reach. Which came first: the tavern or the ferry? We do not know.

Joyce is not a pre-conquest Kentish name, so the person after whom Joyce Green Hospital is named may have come joyously over with the Conqueror in 1066, for many unnamed 'frenchmen' are mentioned in Domesday. Wallenberg traces the name back to a Richard Joce, who appears in the Subsidy Rolls of Kent in 1334.

The name was well established in the 17th century and variously spelt Joyce or Joyes, with or without a green or field. Perhaps he came over on the ferry and chose the first bit of high ground above the worst flood the Thames could muster. There he cleared his patch and grew his first corn, the cattle grazed the marshy meadows and a loop of the uncanalised Darent brought him water aplenty.

Across the River at Purfleet the Bricklayers Arms, hard by the ferry pier, changed its name to Royal Hotel in Victorian times, the better to attract fashionable society, but no Royals are known to have stayed. Nevertheless it is tempting to suppose that 'Prinny', the Prince Regent, a man known to wager large sums on prize fights, may have stayed there on his way to Long Reach, for the tavern became a centre for prize fights whether human or cocks; this must have been good for trade over and above that provided by the bargees and hufflers who helped the barges to navigate Dartford Creek. It was also a safe distance from the arms of both the Kent and Essex law, with a good field of vision in both directions, whereby the beadles could be seen afar off and a quick escape made.

Next to swell the coffers of the ferrymen and landlord were the building workers and staff of the Smallpox Hospital Ships and River Hospitals starting in 1884, but a bit of bother over smallpox and vaccination came too. Occasional overflows of the Thames continued, but the

11

embankment must have been considered adequate in 1911, when the marshes were chosen by Messrs Vickers as an airfield to test their wonderful flying machines — only sometimes they were not all that wonderful. With war came the Royal Flying Corps (RFC) and Long Reach Tavern must have been at the peak of its prosperity, for the buildings of Joyce Green Airfield, as it was called, were erected on its doorstep. A pity for the daring young men in their flying machines that their choice of forced landing, and there were plenty, was between two rivers, a gunpowder factory, drainage dykes, smallpox or fever hospitals and a sewage works. The airfield closed in 1919 but not before it had been the testing ground for the Vickers Vimy, one of which survived the marshy hazards around Joyce Green Airfield only to end up in an Irish bog, after crossing the Atlantic with Alcock and Brown.

Man laid a heavy burden on the marshes when he built a series of power stations at Littlebrook, then by way of compensation dug a hole in the peat and tunnelled to Purfleet, thus finally putting an end to the ferry. In 1899 a plan to make a rail tunnel, using land at Marsh Street Farm, land which the Metropolitan Asylums Board (MAB) had just acquired as a site for Joyce Green Hospital, came to nought. Ninety years on this might be considered a pity, as it could have made a handy place for the channel tunnel rail link to speed under the Thames to the relief of South East London.

Despite declining trade and no airfield the Tavern survived another war, the balcony overlooking the river being much favoured by Joyce Green Hospital wartime staff, but the 'cycle ride back, with ditches on both sides of the road, proved troublesome.

In 1953 the big inundation finally put paid to the Tavern, not least because the raised embankment cut off the view from the balcony. Now new and often noisy uses are being found for the marshes; clay pigeons are shot, young dirt track riders learn their skills and radio-controlled model planes twist and turn where once RFC pilots in their Sopwiths & DHs looped and spiralled during their final three weeks training before getting their 'wings'. Sadly for some, it was literally a crash course, but the hazards that lay ahead in France were much greater.

Three spritsail and one gaff-rigged barge pass reformatory ship *Cornwall* (formerly HMS *Wellesley*), built 1813-15 in Bombay of teak and bombed off Gravesend in September 1940. To the left are the Royal Hotel and Purfleet Magazine. The bargees' causeway to lowtide line was (and is) in front, and the ferry from Long Reach Tavern ended by the Magazine.

12

ABOVE: *Cornwall*, as HMS *Wellesley*, at Chusan, October 1841. (NMM)
CENTRE: 'Stackie' with its deckload of hay, which may have come from
the Hospital (Marsh Street) Farm. The Royal Hotel, Purfleet is at the
back on the left. BELOW: In 1989 the MV *Shah Jehan* is towed past the
Purfleet mooring of the *Cornwall*. (A)

LEFT: A barge tacks past the Hospital Ships with a man at leeboard. Two men could work the barges, except in narrow waters, when hufflers were taken on; hence the pub of that name in Dartford. BELOW: 'Stackie' with a deckload of hay.

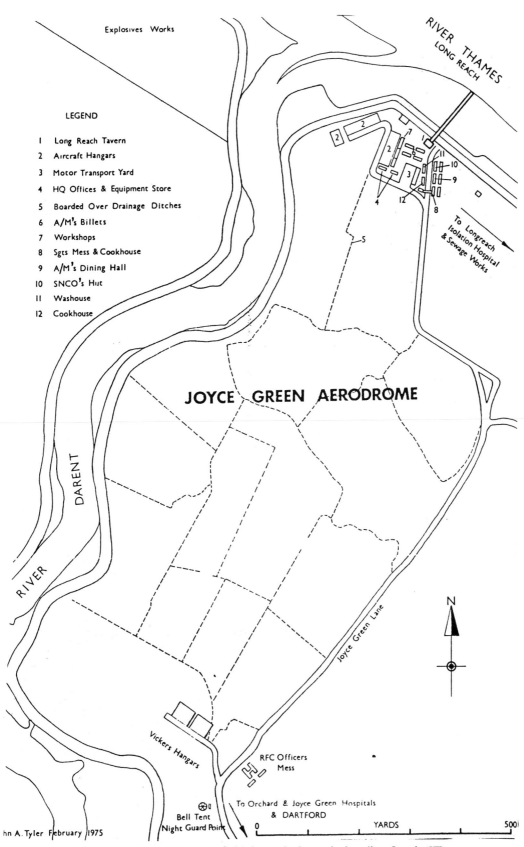

LEGEND

1   Long Reach Tavern
2   Aircraft Hangars
3   Motor Transport Yard
4   HQ Offices & Equipment Store
5   Boarded Over Drainage Ditches
6   A/M's Billets
7   Workshops
8   Sgts Mess & Cookhouse
9   A/M's Dining Hall
10   SNCO's Hut
11   Washouse
12   Cookhouse

Explosives Works

RIVER THAMES
LONG REACH

To Longreach
Isolation Hospital
& Sewage Works

JOYCE GREEN AERODROME

RIVER DARENT

Joyce Green Lane

N

Vickers Hangars

RFC Officers
Mess

Bell Tent
Night Guard Point

To Orchard & Joyce Green Hospitals
& DARTFORD

0   YARDS   500

hn A. Tyler February 1975

This plan of Joyce Green airfield shows the hazards the pilots faced. (JT)

15

ABOVE: Parade Ground and Tavern. (DL) BELOW: Long Reach Hospital and the adjacent sewage works with seepage pits, before the 1935 alterations.

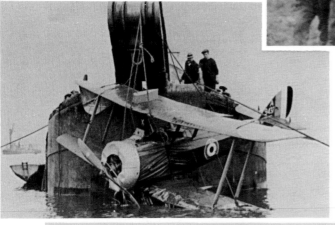

RIGHT: The offensive DH2 that landed in the sewage. (DL) LEFT: This plane, a DH5, found a watery grave in the Thames in 1917 (DL) BELOW: A tidal surge breaches Long Reach embankment by the sewage works, 31 January 1953. (WP)

ABOVE: Morning breaks on 1 February 1953, as two men inspect the damage. (WP) BELOW: Flooded Long Reach Hospital, with a breach in the wall. On the left is the causeway to Joyce Green, along which the gate porter fled, 'pursued by a wall of water'. (WP)

HOW THE HOSPITALS CAME

'The Assyrian came down like the wolf on the fold,
And his cohorts were gleaming in purple and gold.'
Destruction of Sennacherib, Byron

London's Metropolitan Asylums Board (MAB) was set up to administer the newly formed Metropolitan Asylums District (MAD) in 1867. To form the MAD, the parishes and Poor Law Unions of the metropolis were combined for the reception and relief of London rate-aided poor suffering from smallpox, fever or insanity. Here we are concerned with the smallpox side of their responsibilities, for it was for that purpose that Dartford's River Hospitals were built. Thus, in theory any self-supporting citizens who entered an MAB hospital as patients were deprived of their civil rights. In no time at all however, paupers, princes and professors were eligible for admission to the smallpox hospitals of the MAB without question, for there was nowhere else to go and isolation from the general populace was the overriding consideration. Having failed through opposition to find suitable sites for smallpox hospitals in the MAD, the MAB decided to go farther afield and, after years of arguing and lawsuits, they settled on a floating hospital at Long Reach on the Thames between Erith and Greenhithe on the Kent shore, with Purfleet in Essex to the north and Dartford three miles inland to the south. This was a natural decision, for in 1881 they had set up an emergency tented hospital in the grounds of their asylum at Darenth near Dartford.

By 1883 the MAB was buying land at Long Reach and at Gore Farm Darenth for its smallpox hospitals, and at Long Reach they purchased eight and a quarter acres of land for the sum of £1,000 from a Mr Solomon. They brought this land because it was abreast of their hospital ships. 'At this point of the river there is but little foreshore' they wrote 'and the water rapidly deepens so that at comparatively little cost a suitable pier can be constructed, from which convalescent patients can be disembarked at any time and be conveyed to the contemplated hospital at Darenth'.

The smallpox ships were the former naval vessels *Atlas* and *Endymion*, and the twin-hulled *Castalia*, originally intended for the cross-channel service. No one, it seems, objected to the purchase at Long Reach but Mr Fleet, the local landowner, sought an injunction restraining the MAB's activities at Darenth. The injunction failed and Dartford seems to have made no attempt to oppose the concentration of smallpox hospitals in the district; after all they were good for trade. And in March 1884 the MAB awarded contracts to local tradesmen for bread, flour, meat and fish, but there were problems as noted by Dr Ricketts, the Medical Superintendent (MS) in June 1894. 'In consequence of the unfounded charges that have been made against the hospital from time to time, of conveying infection through the staff, I have requested the Matron not to engage in future any women who reside in the neighbourhood'.

19

So it was that supplies and staff had to be brought down from London in the ambulance steamers, but this proved unsatisfactory for a variety of reasons. In August up to 25% of eggs were bad, and milk arrived sour or turned sour soon after arrival; hardly surprising considering that it may have started life on a farm near Dartford, travelled up to SE London, only to come down again, and taking two days in the process.

For staff the main inconvenience was the cessation of the Sunday evening steamer when the hospital was not busy. 'A large number of the staff have leave of absence on Sundays' wrote Dr Ricketts in November 1894; 'most come from London and have to walk from Dartford Station which is not pleasant at night during the winter months and is an added expense'.

Between epidemics, often months at a time, the ships might be empty and they reverted to local purchase and staff recruitment, only for the problem to recur during the next epidemic. It had to be remembered, as Dr Ricketts explained, that a smallpox hospital was peculiarly under the public eye, and any error peculiarly liable to be the subject of public comment, and that was so until the closure of Long Reach in 1973. At the time of the last patients in 1972, an engineer known to have just finished a turn of duty there was shunned by a few nervous folk; if they saw him in the street they would cross over and pass by on the other side.

Back in 1894, the MAB purchased Marsh Street Farm and part of the Joyce Green Estate for a combined price of £22,500. This was subject to the admission into the contemplated hospital of smallpox victims from Dartford Urban and Rural Districts and Union Workhouse. Thus Joyce Green was welcomed since it absolved Dartford from providing its own smallpox unit and was well separated from the town by a mile of green fields on Temple Hill. The service was not free and the UDC & RDC both put in counterclaims for road damages during construction of the River Hospitals. In the end the MAB had to cough up a sum of over £300.

In 1901, with a new epidemic, the transfer of many convalescent patients from the ships to Gore Farm through the outskirts of Dartford was a cause of friction, and Dr Ricketts was urging the MAB to complete the new hospital, now christened Joyce Green (in preference to Marsh Street Hospital perhaps).

An unexpected worry came from the Dartford Postmaster, who said that letters and cards from the ships might infect his staff. Dr Ricketts replied that there was a greater risk to the postal staff from letters from the Dartford area, where there had been a number of cases (of smallpox), than from the ships where the letters had been disinfected. 'I think' he continued 'that on that account you would be very wise to have your whole staff revaccinated'.

Gore Farm Convalescent Smallpox Hospital. View from Darenth Asylum, c1900.

20

ABOVE: Gore Farm seen from the track to the Asylum. BELOW: MAB
horse ambulance, 1883 design, used to convey patients from Long Reach
to Gore Farm. The guards were from the Corps of Commissionaires.

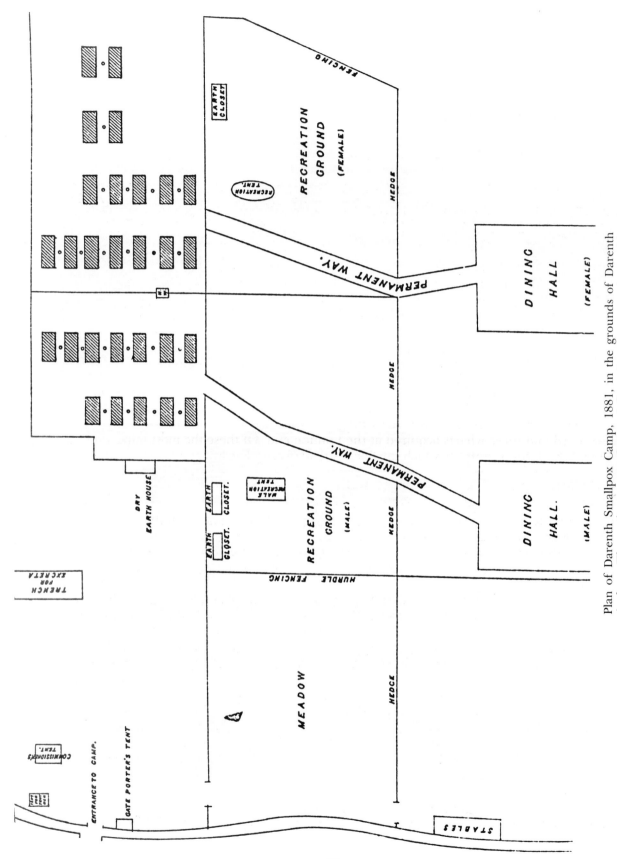

Plan of Darenth Smallpox Camp, 1881, in the grounds of Darenth Asylum. The patients came by road from London, sometimes with unofficial stops for refreshment. (DA)

River Ambulance & Tramway

'Growltiger was a Bravo Cat who travelled on a barge,
In fact he was the roughest cat that ever roamed at large.
From Gravesend up to Oxford he pursued his evil aims,
Rejoicing in his title of The Terror of the Thames.'
                                                    T. S. Eliot

In the 1880s, when this story begins, the River Thames was busy and dirty and no birds flew, unlike the flies which were a regular summer torment on the ships. The river was the natural line of communication for those who lived on or near it, so the decision to use ambulance steamers was probably an easy one to make, once it had been decided to put the floating smallpox hospital at Long Reach. Accordingly in 1884 a fleet of ambulance steamers was assembled and three wharfs acquired at the London end. Of these the most important was South Wharf Rotherhithe, to which smallpox patients were taken by ambulance steamer from North or West London and by land ambulance for local patients in South London. So the South Wharf was like an antenna of the river hospitals, with the body 15 miles distant at Long Reach. At busy times a Medical Officer was stationed at South Wharf to examine the patients, otherwise the Medical Superintendent had to go there by ambulance steamer from Long Reach. From time to time Dr Ricketts complained to the Managers that he could not go when he had patients under treatment at Long Reach until arrangements had been made for a Medical Officer to relieve him; and he instanced April 1900 when, on four days in succession, he was so prevented. This relieving MO usually came from Gore Farm Hospital but problems arose when they too were short-staffed. Conditions at South Wharf were far from ideal as Dr Ricketts made quite clear to the Managers. The receiving room measured 12 x 9 feet, only six inches longer than a stretcher and it had to accommodate four persons as well as the patient. 'The only source of heat is a smoking stove, the lighting is inadequate, the floor and walls are made of rough wood. Here the patients are undressed and labelled and examined minutely. Hence, patients not suffering from smallpox are unnecessarily exposed to the disease'. He recommended the installation of electric light in the receiving room and in two of the ambulance steamers, the *Maltese Cross* and the *Albert Victor*. He further pointed out that the Ambulance Steamers were moored at the Wharf and were used for the reception of patients until such time as they were able to start for the ships. 'In foggy weather they are so used for days at a time. The wards of the steamers are low and of course badly lit. On dark days artificial light is necessary in the day time and under all circumstances the only light available is that given by Colza oil lamps'.

Charles Thomson, an engineer and the Superintendent of River Services, gave an example of the way in which the weather could disrupt the service, and in February 1895 it did it with a vengeance. 'Gentlemen, owing to a dense fog on the 9th inst the SS *Albert Victor* was unable to proceed to Long Reach till the 10th. This steamer started for the hospital ships but on arrival at Bugsby's Reach was unable to make headway due to the vast amount of ice on the river, the weight of which added to the strength of the tide actually drove the steamer astern. The Captain was therefore obliged to let the vessel go with the tide and return to South Wharf. Since the 10th inst. the ice floes have daily increased in number and size to such an extent that the river is only navigable by screw vessels with heavy plating. There is also a great risk to vessels passing up and down owing to the number of derelict barges drifting with the tide. The patients which had arrived at South Wharf since 10th inst have been placed in the hospitals of the steam ship *Geneva Cross* which has been moored at the end of the pier at South Wharf for this purpose, and I have constructed a sort of outer bulwark with baulks of timber and thick planking on the side of the steamer to avoid damage from derelict barges.' Eventually the *Geneva Cross* reached Long Reach on 23 February with 35 patients on board, some of whom had been there for two weeks. Things were very different on 19 June at 2.30 pm when Professor Smith and 13 friends, as Charles Thomson put it, visited South Wharf to inspect the shelters and the receiving rooms, and then proceeded in the *Geneva Cross* to the hospital ships, returning to South Wharf at 7.35 pm. This gives a good idea of the time taken by a round trip of about 30 miles and a tour of inspection using the ambulance steamer from Rotherhithe. They had refreshments on board the *Geneva Cross*, brought up that morning from the *Endymion*, and Dr Ricketts did not forget to order beer, 'and possibly whiskey', so the party must have been quite convivial. The trip demonstrates the multipurpose use of the ambulance steamers for staff, stores and visitors, including applicants for jobs. They all went down by the river when the boats were running but the service was suspended when the ships were empty; the train from Cannon Street was the recommended route, and with luck a hospital conveyance would be at the station to meet them. If not, it was a two mile walk across the marshes using the track leading to Long Reach tavern. At busy times separate steamers were used for patients and visitors, and in 1902 the *Albert Victor* was particularly useful for this run as she had just been converted to a clean ship and could carry up to 300 recovered patients, staff or visitors. After 1897 the pinnace *White Cross* was available when there was only a handful of patients, and in 1919 she was by far the busiest running 3,621 miles out of a total of 5,000 miles for the whole fleet.

The *Red Cross* had spent much of the war ferrying workers to and from Woolwich Arsenal. She returned to South Wharf on 30 October 1919 after reconditioning had been completed. Mr C. E. Sullivan, the Engineer Surveyor, reported that the whole of the vessel had been repainted, the interior of the hospital having been finished in white enamel throughout.

In epidemic times problems arose with the evening steamer. On 11 November 1901 Dr Ricketts wrote 'I understand the Captain of this steamer has received instructions to moor the steamer at the *Castalia* landing stage and not to disembark the patients until the following morning. The plan of not disembarking the patients late at night is generally speaking convenient to the administration of the hospital but in some instances it is desirable that some patients be removed to the wards immediately. Yesterday night for example the removal to the wards of three patients on board was considered advisable, but the master of the vessel informed the medical officer that his orders did not permit removing the vessel and proceeding to the *Atlas* in order that the patients might be disembarked. Under some pressure and after some delay the master at last agreed to move his vessel'. The late steamer only ran in epidemics and it is some 28 years before we hear of another such incident. A former member of the hospital staff recalled that his uncle had smallpox about 1930 and was brought down from South Wharf on a foggy night, arriving at Long Reach pier at 2.00 am, where there was a shemozzle with the shore staff about off-loading the patients at that hour. This time it was the ship's crew who wanted to get rid of the patients and the hospital staff who were resisting, only too understandable as it meant loading and transporting them on the mile long tramway to Joyce Green. Either they had to harness the horses or call out the driver of the motor vehicle which now usually pulled the tram ambulance. From about September 1930 it was all over, for the ambulance steamers stopped running and the patients came down by road, but not before many a Bermondsey boy or girl in the 1920s had 'gone down the river with fever', to use an established phrase of the time. To the end the ambulance steamers must have been more comfortable than the road ambulances which replaced them, and in 1913 Dr Ricketts rose successfully to their defence, extending their working life by 17 years.

By 1913, to meet the changing pattern, South Wharf Rotherhithe was used for fever cases and North Wharf Blackwall redesignated a smallpox receiving and diagnosing station. In that year the river ambulance service carried 1,368 from London and 13 more on the return journey, which suggests a negative death rate; but presumably some patients had arrived by land ambulance and returned by steamer. The service struggled on through the 1920s; repairs and maintenance predominated in the Superintendent's reports, with one or more steamer out of service much of the time and the MAB reluctant to spend more than was absolutely necessary. Superintendent Charles Thomson retired in 1904 and was replaced by C. E. Sullivan, who retired on 30 June 1932, by which time the LCC had been the owners for two years. Extracts from his later reports indicate clearly the problems he had to face. '28 September 1926. As per instructions I submit specifications for the survey of the engines and paddle wheels of the *Albert Victor*'. Repairs were delayed till February 1927 and completed on 23 March, but things were not right for, on 20 April, the *Albert Victor* again went into dry dock for survey and repair. Finally, on 6 May Mr Sullivan reported that the vessel was in good condition. Little is known of her subsequent movements, if any, till April 1931 when she was transferred to the LCC's mooring at Woolwich Ferry 'for the purpose of inspection by intending buyers'. As she was the first to go it may be assumed that she was still in good working order and a saleable proposition. So ended 47 years as an ambulance steamer.

On 26 November 1926 a barge collided with the *Red Cross*, damaging some of the decking, and on 11 December the tug *Lizard*, with barges in tow, collided with the *White Cross*, damaging the rails and bulwark plate. 'Repairs are in hand at the instance of the insurance company' wrote Mr Sullivan, for whenever there was an insurance claim the repairs were quickly done, in marked contrast to routine maintenance. An increasing hazard was the wash of fast-moving steam boats which was especially liable to damage the paddles and their coverings when the steamers were at South Wharf Pier. This extended 300 feet from the Wharf into the main channel of the river so that the ambulance steamers would still be afloat at low tide.

But the service ended with a flourish, as Dr Cameron indicates in his report for January 1930. 'The rise in the number of admissions has brought the river ambulance service into use and one boat has been run since the 7 January. A further rise in admissions could make a second boat necessary in the near future, and I am afraid it would be impossible to avoid making the journey after night fall on account of the time the majority of patients arrive at the Wharf and the limited accommodation on the Wharf'. This would be North Wharf, for South Wharf was now reserved for fever patients. But first they had to appoint a master, for the LCC were due to take over from the MAB in April 1930 and had made it clear that they were going to close the service. Mr Sullivan reported in his letter of 14 January 1930 that, in response to the application made to the LCC, a master named F. Norton had been selected. All was now ready for the final flourish, which came in the period 8 May to 2 July, when 1,117 patients were sent to Joyce Green by steamer and only 19 by road. The last 74 patients to go down the river did so between 24 July and 22 October, during which time 544 went by road. It is doubtful if the 74 realised they were making history but they probably had a smoother journey than the 544 who went by road, at least until they were transferred to the tramway, which was by now a real rock-and-roll system with a distinct possibility of derailment.

The final farewell to the Ambulance Steamers was delayed until early in 1933 when Mr E. G. Giblin, the LCC Official in Charge, made the last entry in the River Ambulance Steamer Report Book. 'Ladies and Gentlemen, I beg to report the following. The steamer *Geneva Cross* left South Wharf on 1 February, the *Maltese Cross* on the 28 February, and the *Red Cross* on 6 March for mooring at Erith preparatory to disposal after being disinfected and certified as such for the Port Sanitary Authority. The first two proceeded under their own steam, with the *Red Cross* in tow as instructed by the Chief Engineer.'

The major drawbacks of the paddle ambulance steamers were that they were immobilised by fog and ice floes; they were vulnerable to flotsam and jetsam and easily damaged by impact with dock fixtures, either from their own momentum, or by the wash from screw-driven steamers which were steadily replacing the old Thames barges. The internal combustion engine and improved roads put the final nail in their coffins. But Dr Ricketts had been a staunch believer in the ambulance steamers and in his valedictory report in 1913 he sang their praises thus: 'Land ambulances, motor ambulances especially, are objectionable necessities — desperate expedient to be avoided when anything else offers. It is open to observation that patients arrive at the Wharf fatigued by the land journey and arrive at Long Reach refreshed by the river. The only other objection that I have heard urged against the river route is that the patients may suffer from exposure and thereby become more liable to such complications as albuminuria and nephritis. They are not exposed. Besides, the statement can be tested by statistical evidence and there is no foundation for it.' But it is doubtful if even he in 1930 would have been able to halt the march of time, and defy the authority of the LCC.

The tramway is a good example of forward planning, in that it was completed in 1897 in advance of the shore-based hospitals, so as to be ready should the rapid construction of a temporary hospital prove necessary, as indeed happened when the 1902 epidemic broke out. The tramway, usually horsedrawn, survived until the demise of the ambulance steamers in 1930; thus it had a working life of 33 years, although no effective use of it was needed until the 1902 outbreak, and then only as far as the adjacent Long Reach Hospital. The MAB was able to build a tramway because in 1896 they had purchased the land necessary for the construction of the River Hospitals. Much of this was Marsh Street Farm, whose house still exists, incorporated in the group of buildings which first housed the Joyce Green trams, the men and horses who operated them, and is now the Transport Department. The original use of the buildings can be made out, with stables, hayloft with hoist, tramsheds with rails and staff cubicles. As far as Dr Ricketts was concerned, building of the tramway presented two problems. The first was vaccination of contractors' men who were working within the Long Reach area. His other was with the new tramway gate in the hospital perimeter fence, as his letter of July 1897 explains: 'On Thursday last I was absent from the hospital for two or three hours and on my return I presented myself at the new gate which opened onto the tramway. I found the gate unlocked and passed in without being observed by the gate porter. I enquired of the gate porter why the gate was unlocked and he informed me that the architect had borrowed the key. I have since enquired of the steward who informs me that Mr Harston, through his clerk, borrowed the key about ten days ago and that he has not yet returned it. Since that date I understand the new entrance gate has remained, as a rule, unlocked.' But worse was to follow, for he discovered that the steward was habitually leaving the hospital without his name being entered in the date book. The steward candidly admitted this and stated that he had to pass through to Marsh Street so frequently during the haymaking season that he would incur an appreciable loss of time and convenience if he always used the old entrance gate or waited for the gate porter to come and unlock the gate for him. 'And I have no doubt in the world but that Mr Moule was acting in perfect good faith. At the same time it appeared to me that Mr Moule's convenience did not entitle us to drive a coach and four through the orders of the Local Government Board. I therefore told him that I thought he was not acting judiciously and asked him to alter his practice; he has not done so.' Mr Moule was able to defy the Medical Superintendent because, as Steward and Shipmaster he was one of the few people in the hospital that the MS could not dismiss instantly. The Steward was top lay manager answerable directly to the MAB and Dr Ricketts' authority over him amounted to no more than requests, which he was powerful enough to turn down or ignore as he saw fit. In the event, by the time Dr Ricketts' storm in a hayloft blew up, haymaking was nearly over, the Steward was able to abandon his unorthodox practice without loss of face, Dr Ricketts' metaphorical coach and four retired back to its own stable and the MAB lay doggo as their own architect was one of the miscreants. As a sequel the MAB Minutes report that Mr Moule was transferred temporarily in 1899 to a fever hospital and is recorded as having a bonus from the Board for taking on this work. In 1903, when Joyce Green opened and the tramway came into its own, the MAB proposed that Mr Moule should automatically be Steward of the enlarged smallpox hospitals, but a move to put the Steward of Gore Farm in, on the grounds of greater experience in the opening of smallpox hospitals, was accepted. However, the Gore Farm Steward turned the post down and Mr Moule was appointed. Could Dr Ricketts have been behind the move to block Mr Moule's return?

In 1904 the tramway was extended to the South Gate of Joyce Green Hospital, bringing the tramway to its maximum extent of 3.4 miles, measured as single track. This was for the conveyance of coal when outside vehicles could not proceed within the hospital beyond the South Gate in epidemic times. After closure of the section from Long Reach in 1930 the trams were used for internal purposes till about 1936, and the track was lifted in 1943 to help the war effort. The stone setts remain and a few short stretches of rail continue to attract the attentions of enthusiasts.

After unfortunate experiences with secondhand tram cars, in 1908 the MAB designed their own purpose-built models, and these were based on detailed specifications submitted by Dr Ricketts. He was so pleased with the design that in 1909 he suggested to the Board they ought to take out a patent, hardly necessary as the horsedrawn ambulances must have been unique. It is hard to conceive of the circumstances under which any hospital would be built on the River Hospital model.

ABOVE: *Geneva Cross* at South Wharf in 1894. Bullivant's warehouse is behind, on the Isle of Dogs. BELOW: The 8-bunked hospital cabin on the *Geneva Cross*.

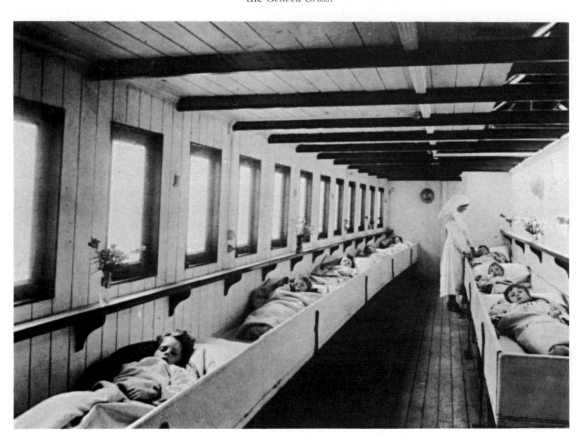

ABOVE: *Albert Victor* at Long Reach pier, ready to return patients to London c1902. BELOW: South Wharf 1902; the pier buildings are beyond the cab shelter. INSET: In 1988 the cab shelter is a shed. All the other buildings have gone. (A)

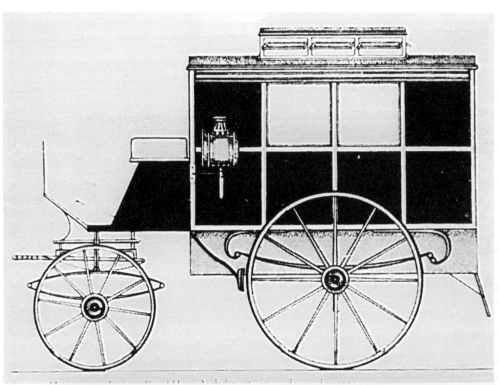

ABOVE: The pride of the MAB land ambulances in 1883. BELOW: The
pride of the MAB land ambulances in 1924.

ABOVE: South Wharf in 1987. The pier extended 300ft into the river. Restored LCC flats behind buildings of the Surrey Docks Farm Provident Society now occupy part of the site. (A) BELOW: The crew of the *Geneva Cross*, including the night watchman. It is probably Capt Livett between the nurses, whose number varied with demand.

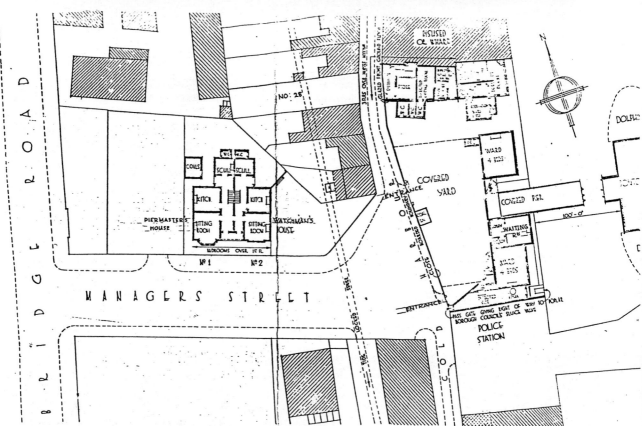

ABOVE: North Wharf Blackwall in 1988: almost unscathed by blitz and time after 50 years of idleness. Nos 1 & 2 Managers Street stood in the vacant site in the foreground, the Police Station on the right. (A) BELOW: A faded plan of North Wharf, as taken over by the LCC in 1930.

ABOVE: On the right: 4-bedded ward; on the left: single bedded lean-to for doubtful cases — a view from the yard under an 80-year-old corrugated iron roof. (A) RIGHT: Coldharbour is as uninviting and narrow as it was 100 years ago, when would-be nurses walked along it to catch the steamer to Long Reach. (A) BELOW: A view of the river at Blackwall. North Wharf pier extended 200ft into the river, and access to it was blocked at times by boats going to the West India dock (behind the camera). The Wharf is hidden by the Police Station, LDDC development and East India dock beyond. (A)

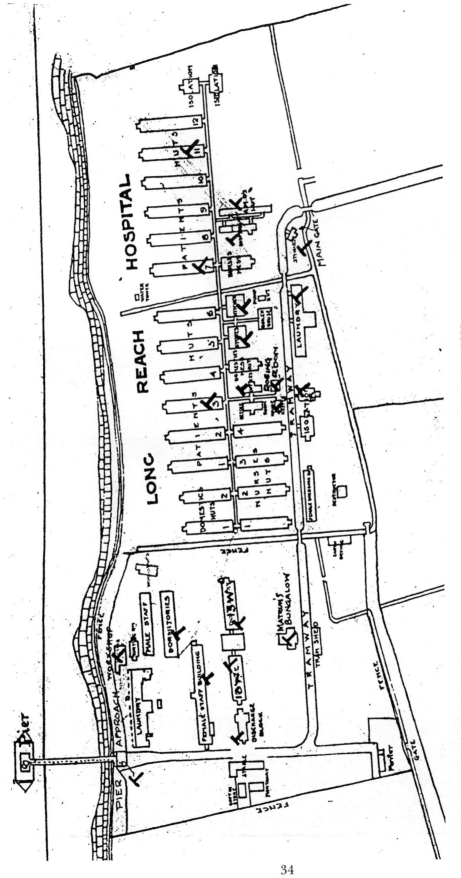

Plan of Long Reach Hospital and pier, c1925.

34

LEFT: *Maltese Cross* and RIGHT: *White Cross* approach Long Reach
c1915. BELOW: The patient is taken ashore, from *Albert Victor*.

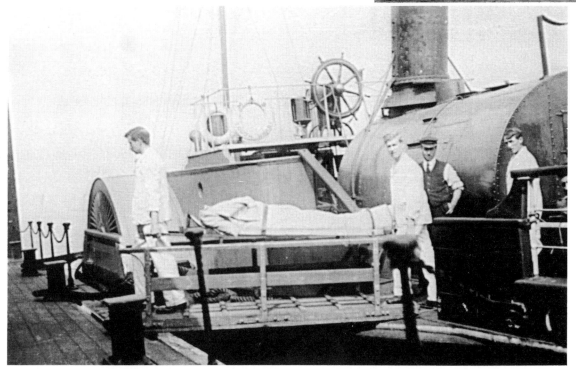

36

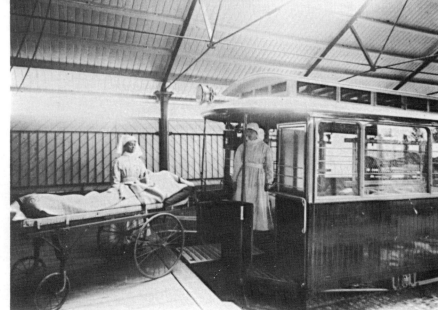

ABOVE: The patient is carried up the pier tunnel and BELOW: put on the horse drawn 'trambulance'
for the mile-long journey to Joyce Green Hospital.

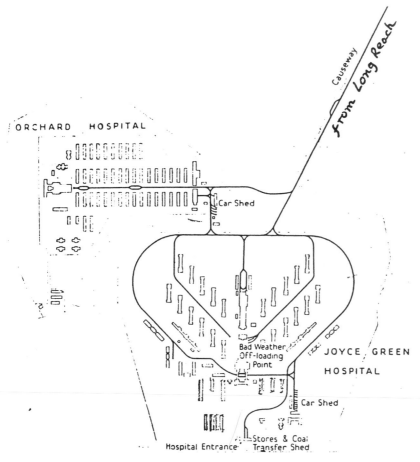

ABOVE: Plan of tramway at maximum extent. BELOW: At Joyce Green
Hospital, Dr A. H. Haddow was in attendance — he was ill at the time
and died soon after 1916.

ABOVE: The 'trambulance' fleet of five in 1930, shortly before closure.
Two have drawbars for motor traction. BELOW: Stables and hayloft in
1988. Stone setts show the position of the rails before removal during the
last war. (A)

ABOVE: The sheds were made for 10 vehicles; these with low roofs were probably for the coal trolleys; a 1987 photo (A) CENTRE: Stabling for five horses is now used for worn-out vehicle parts. (A) BELOW: In 1989, Transport Officer James Taylor and assistant Denise Penfold work in the saddleroom, with its original panelling, a new coat of varnish and old screw marks. (A)

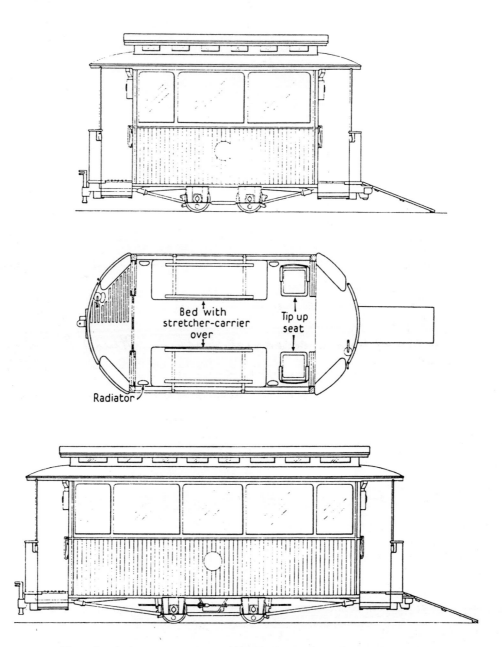

Bed with
stretcher-carrier
over

Tip up
seat

Radiator

Plan of ambulances, based on a design by Dr Ricketts. OPPOSITE: The
report of the Superintendent of Ambulance Steamers for 28 November
1892.

South Wharf
Rotherhithe S.E
28 November 1892

The Ambulance Committee

Gentlemen

I have received an offer for the old
boat which was formerly in use at the West Wharf
and I recommend that the offer be accepted —
I submit same herewith — there is also a quantity
of old rope and fire bars in store which I recommend
should be sold

On the 17 inst I engaged Arthur Henry Rankin
Age 25 Single as Night Watchman (Asst Fireman) at
the West Wharf in lieu of Henry Thomas Watson who
was temporarily appointed and was discharged on the
12th inst —

On the 18 inst the "Albert Victor" left S. Wharf at 5.40 pm
with an adult male patient for the Hospital Ships
On this Steamer arriving just below Woolwich the
fog came on very thick and Capt. Livett was obliged
to anchor — At 8.0 am the following morning the
fog lifted and the Steamer proceeded to Long Reach
arriving at 9.25 am — A nurse from the S.E. Hospital
was in charge of the patient who was able to walk
from the Ambulance to the Hospital of the Steamer.

41

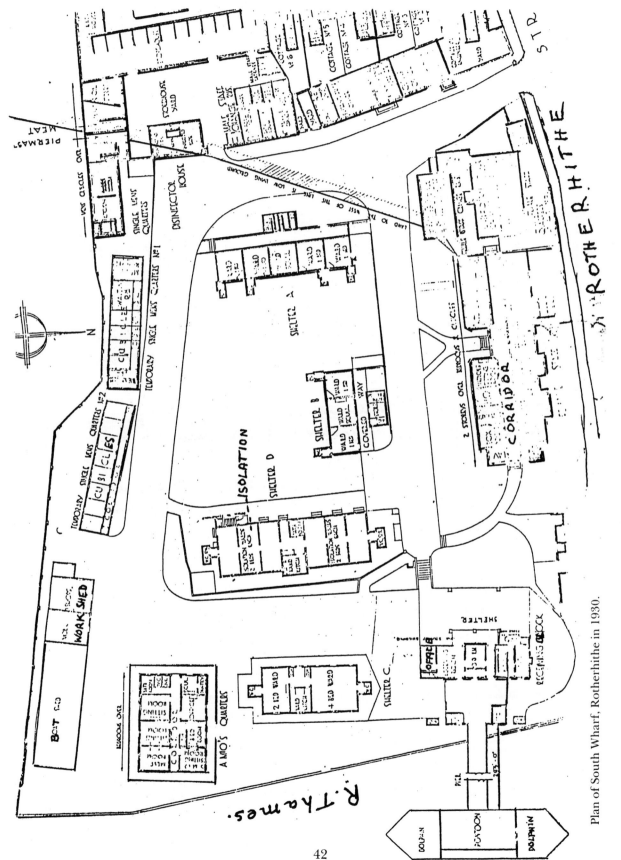

Plan of South Wharf, Rotherhithe in 1930.

42

South Wharf
Rotherhithe SE 16
Jan 17/28

To/
The River Ambulance Sub. Committee

Ladies & Gentlemen,
Further to my report re flooding at South Wharf of the 8th inst. The roads have been reframed by the Engr-in-Chiefs dept. Messrs Norman contractors carrying out the work & the wharf was available for the admission of Patients on Sat. 14th inst: & on the 10th use in accordance with instructions 1 cwt of coal was issued to the tenant of each staff cottage for the purpose of drying up the property. Apart from the removal of creosote oil & the drying off of certain stores, the work of which is now in hand conditions are now normal.

On Wed Dec 28th the Geneva Cross went into Dry dock for Survey & overhaul & returned on completion of repairs to South Wharf Jan 10.

In accordance with instructions estimates were invited from 3 firms for the repair of 12 clocks. as under:
Messrs Gabriel. Sudfall Hill
  „   Brampton
  „   Geelde. Rotherhithe

The report of the Superintendent of Ambulance Steamers for 17 January 1928.

43

Castalia at Dover; artist's impression of what might have been.

THE HOSPITAL SHIPS

'The Thrush . . . lays close to the Endymion,
between her and the Cleopatra, just to the
eastward of the sheer hulk.'
Jane Austen in *Mansfield Park*, Chap 38.

There were three ships, the *Atlas* and *Endymion*, both sheer hulks, and the *Castalia*, the *Endymion* being the one in the middle and used for administration purposes. It had been a 50-gun 3,000 ton frigate, was acquired by the Board in 1881 and sold in 1904 as scrap at the same time as the others. Nothing is known of its service life but it can hardly have been the one referred to by Jane Austen 70 years earlier. The *Atlas* was a 100-gun ship of the line of the Nelson class, built in 1870 at Chatham but never fully commissioned, as by that time it was out of date with the advent of ironclads and modern gunnery; the Admiralty must have been glad to get rid of it after 11 years, an unwanted and unloved hulk lying off Chatham. Its two gun decks were readily converted into wards, roughly one bed replacing one gun, the rings being left in place. The deck height is given as seven feet but, with beams and other things, including electric light bulbs, it must often have been 'duck your heads', especially for those over six feet. Conversion of the orlop deck for beds and the addition of an isolation hut on the main deck brought the accommodation to somewhere between 110 and 150, the MAB favouring the higher figure. Dr Ricketts was continually resisting pressure by the Board to increase the number of beds from his lower figure, but in times of an epidemic he had to give way. When fully commissioned the *Atlas* would have had a single screw plus sail, a double mode of propulsion, which led to the naval command 'up funnel down screw'. One of its sister ships, the *Agamemnon*, laid the first Atlantic cable in 1858. After conversion the *Atlas* was initially moored at Deptford and brought down to Long Reach in 1882.

The *Castalia* was quite a different kettle of fish; she was built as a twin-hulled vessel in 1874 for the cross-channel services but, after tests, the riding was found to be too rough, even though rolling in big seas was reduced, so she never sailed out of Dover, but lay idle for 10 years before taking up her station at Long Reach. The double hull was two Thames barges secured side by side, and on these they put five ward blocks arranged in echelon to improve the lighting and ventilation, similar to the layout adopted for the wards at Joyce Green. Wards 1 to 5 had ceilings seven and a half feet high but in wards 6 to 10, which may have been in the upper storey, they were 17 feet. The total bed compliment, like the *Atlas*, was officially 150, of which six were reserved for delirious patients (ward 8) and a two bedded isolation ward which may have been one of the end blocks. Unfortunately, no photographs of the inside of this intriguing ship have survived. In 1878 the *Castalia*, an unwanted hulk in Gallions Reach, had been a silent witness of the *Princess Alice* paddle steamer disaster off Becton gasworks, but in 1893 it was her turn to be hit by a steamer (SS *Barrowmore*), without loss of life, for she was empty at the time.

Once the ships were moored the question arose — should they be supplied and staffed by locals or must everything be brought down from London? Local vendors were no doubt delighted with the prospect of increased trade but the local authorities were fearful that this would mean an increase of smallpox in their parishes. Even without trade the non-resident staff such as laundry workers, who travelled to and from the ships, were a potential source of infection, so the local councils were on the lookout for trouble and they did not have long to wait. In the event the trouble arose from the shore leave granted to resident staff from the ships and it was to Erith that they took the liberty boat, the nearest port to Long Reach.

Smallpox cases had been rare in that district, so it is no surprise that local inhabitants were fearful lest the disease spread to them. The death of Miss Willis in March 1885 about two weeks after a dance provided the Erith Local Board (ELB) with the opportunity they sought. The doctor attending her certified she died of malignant smallpox. In a letter to the MAB dated 16 April the clerk of the ELB opened the campaign. 'On Friday evening the 13 March last the Erith Quadrille Assembly gave a tradesman's ball in the public hall. At this ball a Mr Davidson an officer from one of the hospital ships belonging to your Board attended. One of the visitors at the ball with whom Mr Davidson came into contact was Miss Willis of Avenue Road Erith. On the 27 March Miss Willis developed a very bad form of smallpox and died within a few hours of being attacked. A complaint has reached my Board before of the frequency of visits to this neighbourhood by officers and men from the hospital ships, and the Board having investigated the case of Miss Willis are quite unable to trace its origin except as coming from the contact with Mr Davidson, they therefore ask that you make a searching inquiry into this matter.' In his reply, Dr R. A. Birdwood, the first Medical Superintendent of the hospital ships, challenged the diagnosis, having discovered by making inquiries that Miss Willis did not have an eruption and she died after three hours' illness, bringing up blood. He assured the ELB that members of the staff attending the dance had observed the precautions imposed to prevent carrying infection. He explained that, before going out, they were required to take a bath and change their clothes, and that these clothes were kept separate from the clothes they wore in the hospital. He pointed out that it was impractical to place any restriction on the staff after they leave the hospital, and reassured the Local Government Board (LGB), who were also involved, that members of the staff observed the rules respecting the bathing and changing of their clothes. An inquiry took place with depositions by the certifying 'medical man', J. Clarkson Maynard, and Miss Willis's mother, whose evidence cast doubt on Dr Maynard's competence to diagnose malignant smallpox, a diagnosis which she said he only made after he had gone home and read it in a book.

There seems to have been no meeting between the two doctors to discuss the case in a cold, clinical atmosphere; both were advocates of the cause they represented and, while Mrs Willis's statement diminishes the credibility of Dr Maynard, we must agree with him that Dr Birdwood's statement was made on hearsay evidence, albeit he was a smallpox expert.

The MAB were clearly anxious to allay the fears and allegations of Erith, for in their eyes the smallpox ships were a success. They planned to bring all cases of smallpox there and they did not wish to be forced to abandon the scheme as had happened to so many of their previous attempts to establish smallpox hospitals in London. The Local Board thought otherwise and their secretary wrote to the LGB 'My Board have on a previous occasion made complaints to the MAB on the inefficiency of the precautions taken with the workmen employed on the vessels, and although they have not been able until now to establish what is in their opinion a proof of the officers and other attendants from the ships causing the spread of the disease into this district they have a strong conviction that the death of Miss Willis was traceable to the presence of Mr Davidson or other officers at the ball in question. So long as the hospital ships continue at their moorings my Board feel that the strictest precautions should be taken by the Asylums Board, and rules made if necessary and enforced for preventing altogether the visits of officers and others into a populous district.'

They followed this up in July with a request that the ships be moved downstream, having by now learnt that the MAB proposed to abandon the use of the smallpox hospitals in the metropolis and bring all cases to the vessels. Poor MAB. Nobody wanted them and their smallpox, and now Erith wished to consign them to a mooring where, at the best, patients and staff would have seasickness as well as smallpox to contend with, and at worst they might founder with all hands.

Fortunately for the MAB the LGB ignored the suggestion that the ships should be moved downstream nor did they express an opinion as to whether Miss Willis died of smallpox or not. They did, however, agree with a suggestion from the ELB that the necessary stores should be conveyed to the ships in the ambulance steamers instead of by railway. They concluded 'I am to add that the Board think that this proposal deserves the careful consideration of the Managers'. A request couched by the LGB in those terms was, of course, to all intents and purposes an order, and the MAB duly responded by restricting local purchase and using the ambulance steamers to convey stores down from London.

What happened subsequently? The answer seems to be nothing much. The epidemic died away and with it fear, and the ships with their skeleton staff stayed where they were awaiting the next epidemic. Things were so quiet that Dr Birdwood ended his annual report for 1891 on an optimistic note. In response to an invitation from the Managers, about 50 members of the International Congress of Hygiene and Demography had visited the ships on 14 and 15 August, and Dr Birdwood reported ' Your guests were pleased to express their admiration for the provision made by the managers for the Metropolitan Asylums District for the treatment of smallpox epidemics. These expert students of the public health from near and distant lands witnessed the success of a hygienic experiment for on those days London was free of smallpox and there are no patients at the ships. Isolation, disinfection, and vaccination are the three means for checking the spread of smallpox. By searching for the truth about these means and then applying the knowledge gained in practice, you have rendered a great service to the state'. But there was to be one more major outbreak still 10 years away before these could be looked upon as more than just brave words.

The next outbreak was 1893 but numbers had been building up in 1892, the year in which Dr T. F. Ricketts was appointed Medical Superintendent. By 1893 there had been some relaxation in the policy of buying from London and sending down on the ambulance steamers; firstly, in the absence of an epidemic, the steamers did not make regular journeys and secondly, perishable goods, especially milk and eggs, were often bad on arrival. But it was a pair of borrowed trousers that caused Dr Ricketts one of his first big headaches as Medical Superintendent and it was Dartford's turn to do the complaining. They were worried by the high incidence of smallpox locally and submitted a list of 17 cases for Dr Ricketts' comments. One of these was a Mrs Watts, whose husband had been working down at Long Reach. Let Dr Ricketts speak for himself:

'With one exception all these cases are said to have contracted smallpox through a man, Watts, who was warded here for five weeks with a broken leg and who was discharged on 7 November. The theory is that this man infected his wife, that he infected Charles Reed and James Newton by being in their company, and that he infected Peter Thomsett who had lent his flannels to Watts to work in at the Gas Works. Of the above four cases, the first to occur were those of Thomsett, Watt's wife and Humphreys (Edward). The rash on Thomsett appeared on 7 December and the other two on 9 December. Watts was discharged from hospital on 7 November a full calendar month previously and did not go to the ships again until 5 December. Watts, when he was discharged, was treated as a discharged patient; he was based on shore and his clothing was disinfected. We are asked to believe that after these precautions he should carry away infection with him which should remain latent for 16 days and then should develop smallpox of such virulence as to infect four persons in succession. About such a theory it seems to me it is not necessary to argue.' Finally he pointed out that the men worked at the Gas Works, where smallpox had broken out some two weeks previously. 'Under these circumstances to strain after a source of infection here seems a piece of gratuitous ingenuity.' Dr Ricketts didn't mince words when he was certain of his facts.

In 1901, after seven epidemic-free years, local suppliers had regained many contracts, but there were anomalies. For instance, fish came direct from Grimsby, well wrapped in ice we may be sure, whereas in 1894 it had come from G. Vinten, 4 High Street, Dartford; so also in 1901 did ice, now used therapeutically as well as to preserve perishable goods. Milk, often bad in hot weather, continued to come from Brockley in SE London, but meat and vegetables came from Dartford, the latter supplied by the inappropriately named Bacon. But it was the delivery men employed by meat vendor Reuben Message of Dartford who put the cat among the pigeons, or rather let the smallpox out of the isolation bag. They, with the connivance of the Long Reach gate porter, were allowed to take their delivery carts up to the pierhead, on giving a verbal assurance that they had been vaccinated. They had of course been vaccinated only in infancy and had no residual immunity. Thus, when delivery man Graham developed smallpox two to three weeks after these visits, Dr Ricketts had to accept that Graham had been infected in the hospital compound. This transgression of the rules cost the gate porter his job, Reuben Message his contract, and probably Dartford Council their slender confidence that smallpox could be contained within the compound.

Even so, all was not lost to London traders, for Bacon continued to supply potatoes, and a year later Message provided ice to the tune of £67, admittedly small fry compared with the 1902 quarterly account of over £1,000 to a London meat firm. The fruits of a smallpox epidemic were sweet for some and Message must have rued the day that his men crossed the hospital threshold, without first having been revaccinated.

Another way in which the *cordon sanitaire* around the ships could be breached was with the delivery of coal. In 1894 this was done by Salmon of Long Reach Tavern and his two sons, both of whom refused vaccination. Dr Ricketts pointed out that, as these men lived on the river bank and gained access to the hospital by boat, it was practically impossible to keep them off the premises. He therefore requested the Board to write to the contractor to point out to Salmon that he held his contract on the condition that men employed by him should submit to vaccination. That was in October 1894, and by May 1895 the situation still did not seem satisfactory, as the MOH for Dartford claimed that infection was being conveyed there by the ships' staff and by workmen employed unloading coal barges. In reply, Dr Ricketts felt that the only satisfactory plan was to obtain photographs of these men, so that the gate porter might have adequate means of identifying them. The photographs taken of these 15 husky men have survived, stuck in a contemporary scrapbook together with their names, but there are no Salmons so presumably they preferred to lose the work than be vaccinated. The men were all locals, and people living in Dartford have been able to identify some of them as ancestors or friends of the family. In January 1902 it was poetic justice for Salmon, for his sons Ernest, 19, and Albert, 22, were both admitted to the ships with smallpox. They had been vaccinated in infancy, not since.

Despite these efforts to isolate the ships and to prevent unvaccinated people from gaining access, the attitude to visitors was most casual. Indeed, it is a surprise to find that there were any visitors to the patients, but at the beginning of 1903 the MAB was asked to consider the inadequate accommodation provided at the new Joyce Green Hospital for such visitors.

In epidemic times, they were told, visitors arrived in large numbers, over 40 together at the hospital ships on one occasion. There they were provided with a meal before being admitted to the wards. Many arrived unvaccinated, and it is no surprise that there were complaints from Medical Officers of Health that smallpox had been brought back from the ships by them. For instance, at their meeting on 25 January 1902, the Hospital Committee of the MAB replied to a complaint from Dr Allen, MOH for the City of Westminster, by stating that, although every visitor to a patient was strongly pressed to be vaccinated they did not think it possible for the Managers to make vaccination a condition of entry to the hospital. They added that the precaution was taken of forwarding names and addresses of all visitors, whether they accepted vaccination or not, to the MOH of the district in which they lived. But the trouble persisted and on 22 February they considered a letter from the MOH of Epsom, stating that smallpox had been introduced into his district by visitors to the hospital ships, though they themselves were re-vaccinated and escaped the disease, and suggesting the visits should be discouraged as far as possible.

Letters were received from as far away as Rugby, which stated that smallpox had been introduced into the district by a person who, being unvaccinated, visited a patient at the hospital ships and subsequently developed the disease. They entered their emphatic protest against the practice of allowing persons to visit relatives at the ships, except under the protection of re-vaccination. A further loophole to the isolation screen is revealed by the report dated 5 April 1902 of the Contract Committee, concerning the return of empties from smallpox institutions. 'We have given instructions that, for the present, no sheets, matting, packages or other stuffs used as coverings for goods delivered to these establishments are to be returned; also that any crates or cases which, in the opinion of the respective Medical Superintendent, might possibly convey infection are to be retained in the institutions and utilised or destroyed as they may direct.'

At the same time the Essex County Council came up with their particular worry about the possible spread of smallpox *via* sewage discharged from the ships in the river. The Board brushed this aside rather peremptorily. They said they could not agree at the present time to restrict the use of the ships to convalescent cases. The Essex letter seems to have been motivated by the high incidence of smallpox in Purfleet, just across the river, as a letter from the Orsett Union makes clear. It was sent by the local MP, Lieutenant Colonel Tufnell, and reached the MAB *via* the LGB, and in it he claimed the high incidence was due to the smallpox hospital ships, and his solution was their urgent removal.

The crisp answer, which bears the hallmark of Dr Ricketts, was that there was no evidence justifying the assumption that the cases of smallpox referred to were due to the presence of the hospital ships in Long Reach. He further noted that the reformatory ship *Cornwall* moored off Purfleet was free of smallpox, the crew and inmates being fully protected by vaccination, and the same applied to the soldiers of the Purfleet garrison. In fact, the high incidence of smallpox in Purfleet, which was part of the Orsett Poor Law Union, arose out of the activities of antivaccinationists, and it may be Lieutenant Colonel Tufnell himself was one of their leaders, supported by a Mr Beurle, who was the Hackney Union representative on the MAB. Purfleet being in Essex, and therefore outside the MAB area, had no representative on that Board.

A report on the smallpox epidemic in the Orsett Union in 1902 was given in the *British Medical Journal* in 1903 by G. S. Buchanan, and the low vaccination state is clearly laid at the door of a local anti-vaccination league, supported by a guardian and local employer. In Purfleet the case rate was 86.6 per thousand population in a total population of 600, no less than 40% of the houses being invaded by the disease. In these circumstances, the suggestion that the outbreak was caused by aerial infection from the MAB hospital ships half a mile away could not be taken seriously. Many of the men working on the temporary smallpox hospitals at Long Reach and the Orchard were probably housed in Purfleet and travelled over daily on the ferry, so Dr Ricketts must have been only too painfully aware of the paramount importance of vaccinating all such workers.

In 1901 the MAB reviewed the future of the hospital ships. They listed the disadvantages: first, the cost of maintenance at £9,500 per annum for dry dock inspection; second, the danger of fire, at least two fires having occurred, and they recalled that the naval hospital ship *Goliath* was burnt to the ground with great loss of life; third, danger of delirious persons jumping overboard, two patients having done so; fourth, danger from weather and collision with other ships (in 1898 a steamer the *Barrowmore* collided with the *Castalia* and the wash from large vessels had broken the electric cable from the shore); fifth, the difficulty in expanding accommodation, which the Board considered was normally 300, but which Ricketts thought should be 220. In the event, in an emergency a maximum of 400 was reached.

Not surprisingly, 80 or more years after the closure, no first-hand account of the ships can be got, but interesting local folklore images survive. In February 1974 an elderly female patient asked for literature on the coffin ships and in March 1980 a schoolgirl aged 13 wrote an essay 'The Prison Ship'. This was passed onto the hospital authorities by her schoolmaster who commented 'this is really fascinating, it is also beautifully written. I had not read something so well composed for a long time'. Nor, one might add, so inaccurate, yet passed on as gospel truth. Here are extracts:

'All Gran remembered was being carried at the dead of night in a red blanket by her parents through Greenhithe down to the water front. Then she was taken by rowing boat out to a big ship moored off Greenhithe Reach.

'The ship was a hulk and had been used as a prison ship but now it was used as a quarantine ship for smallpox.

'Gran remembered years later that it was huge on the outside but very small on board, cramped with low ceilings and strong doors with a small shuttered window in each. It was dark and filthy. There were even rats on board which you could hear scampering about during the night. It smelt awful of sulphur candles that were burnt to kill the smallpox germ, and of sweating people.

'These people and Gran slept on wooden slatted beds, no mattresses, and they had no medical people to take care of them. Patients that were better and that had got over smallpox looked after the rest. People stayed on that ship for three weeks and if after that time you were still alive a rowing boat was sent by relations out to the hulk. This ferryman was paid, and had to be paid well. He would call out your name for you.

'Gran remembered vividly the day the ferryman came and called "Clare Emma Couchman age 10, are you alive?" She shouted back "Yes" and then had to strip off and put on a new gown sent by her mother.

Gran still bore the pox marks till the day she died.'

The ship was probably the *Atlas*, as the description of the ward deck is convincing and sulphur was used to fumigate. Furthermore the *Atlas* was moored off Greenhithe in 1881, prior to moving upstream to Deptford to complete her refitting as a hospital ship. The presence of the sheer hulk at Greenhithe was obviously the basis for the halftrue stories that her bulky presence stimulated in local minds. The patients did not lie on wooden slats for, in September 1901, Dr Ricketts reported that 230 feather beds were in use and some hair mattresses added to make up the beds available on the ships to 250. This was at the outbreak of the epidemic and, in 1899, an inter-epidemic year, Dr Ricketts reported the bedding was badly infested with moth, but still usable. Then in July 1901, one month before the epidemic hit them, he reported that the position had worsened 'Many of the coverings are spoilt and the feathers inside are foul . . . I do not think the feathers are ruined hopelessly, and if they were cleaned they could be used again'.

In 1904 the ships were sold for scrap for about £8,000, and the proceeds used to defray the cost of additional bathing and disinfecting accommodation at Joyce Green. For 18 years they had played their part and fully earned their salt in the fight against smallpox.

ABOVE: Smallpox Hospital Ships, *Atlas*, *Endymion* and *Castalia* (nearest camera). The reformatory ship *Cornwall* is in the background. BELOW: *Castalia* with double hull and wards in echelon; gangway to *Endymion* on the left.

ABOVE: *Castalia* in dry dock in 1898 for repair, after being hit by SS *Barrowmore.* The cost was £1,500. BELOW: *Atlas,* with figurehead facing towards London. Long Reach floating pier is on the right.

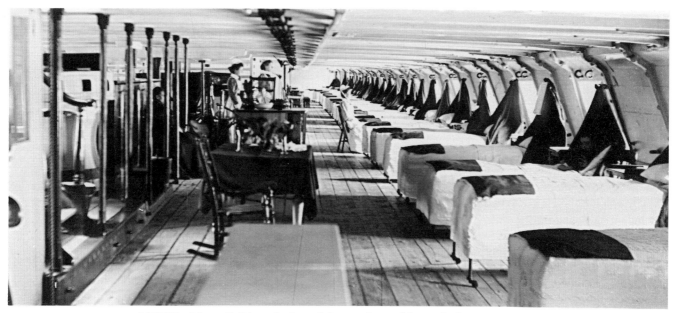

ABOVE: *Atlas:* a full-length view of the ward, roughly one bed per gun.
BELOW: Inside *Atlas.* Note the gun rings, light bulb, and rough floor
timbers.

ABOVE: The crew of *Atlas*. The man with the beard is probably the mate. The post of Shipmaster was held by the Hospital Steward (not present). One man was graded fitter/electrician and paid 34s per week plus unfurnished quarters, gas, washing and uniform. BELOW: Seated (centre) is Dr Ricketts and his assistants. Standing (centre) is Steward A. B. Moule with his assistants. Both photos are on the deck of *Atlas*.

ABOVE: Dr Ricketts, Assistant Matron Louisa Barton and nurses on the deck of *Atlas*. Dr Ricketts has adorned himself with pocket hankie and buttonhole, but wears the same tie as in the photo with the Steward. The nurse behind him has adorned her cross with safety pins. BELOW: Two of the 15 men allowed to bring coal on board ship in 1895. LEFT: Wm Fitchett alias Norman and RIGHT: Wm Fitchett snr.

Three more Coalmen: LEFT: Alfred Watts. CENTRE: Thomas Watts, and RIGHT: Thomas Newton. BELOW: Thomas Newton (seated with peaked cap), about 40 years after the identification photos were taken. The men had been revaccinated or had had smallpox, but no certain pockmarks are visible. (SB) OPPOSITE ABOVE: Electricity engine, onshore, for ships' lights, installed by Simplex Electrical Syndicate. Some of the men lodged at Purfleet before 'rations & lodging' were provided on site; 3s a day for mechanics and 2s for labourers. CENTRE: The plate reads, Edison Hopkinson Dynamo No 96. It was made by James Johnston & Co of Manchester and installed in 1886. The first workable bulbs were made by Swan (1878) and Edison (1879). BELOW: The big frost of February 1898. The steamers could not come down from London for two weeks and the temperature fell below 40°F on the *Castalia*. The screw tug went to and from Long Reach pier with supplies.

METROPOLITAN ASYLUMS BOARD.

HOSPITAL SHIPS.

Matron's Record of Service and Conduct of the undermentioned Officer or Servant.

Name in full	*8.7.h. 347: 17.11.22.* Ella Lizzie Houndsfield Elles
Age... ... ... *Date of Birth*	24th May 1874 20 years
Position held	2nd Asst Nurse. 1st Asst Promoted Charge Nurse
Date of Appointment	30th May 1894 *Night Superintendent 8th Oct. 1907* *24 Feb 1902* *Housekeeper 22nd March 1911*
Date of Leaving	31st October 1926.
Cause of Leaving	Superannuated.

REMARKS.

To include a record of behaviour, with a statement whether ever reported to the Sub-Committee for any offence or misconduct, and a record of result of Sub-Committee's investigation.

Promoted 1st Asst Nurse 2nd July 1895

Lent to the Smallpox Hospital Gloucester from
16th May 1896 to the 24th July 1896 where she
rendered valuable service.

Transferred to Gore Farm Hospital 8th Sept 1896

Retransferred to Ship 9th Feb 1897

Transferred to Gore Farm Hospital 6th Dec 1897

Retransferred to Ships 15th Jan 1898

Transferred to Gore Farm Hospital 24th Oct 1898

Retransferred to Ships from Park Hospital 28th April 1899

Transferred to River Ambulance Service 15th July 1899

Transferred to Gore Farm 1st Nov 1899

Retransferred to Hospital Ships 14 Nov 1899

Special leave *2 months* granted through illness Nov 14 1900.

Returned to Ships Feb 14th 1901

1 bk. 200 lvs. 11/01. 222. 326a. Transferred to Office of Charge Nurse Feb 26th 1908.

A Most valuable and efficient Officer.

Entry in Record of Service Book kept by Matron Wacher.

Nurses

'Let us now remember many honourable women
Such as bade us turn again when we were like to die.'
From *Dirge of Dead Sisters* by R. Kipling.

'God Bless Miss Nightingale,
May she be free from strife.
These are prayers
Of the poor soldier's wife.'
Crimean popular song.

Florence Nightingale (FN) was 64 when the ships opened for smallpox and past the peak of her post-Crimean organising frenzy. Her name does not appear in the minutes of the MAB but it does in the pages of Matron Wacher's female staff register, for there were 39 Florences listed between 1895 and 1913 out of a total of 1,175 female staff on the register, about half being nurses. The oldest Florence on the list was born in 1873, when FN was 53, and the youngest saw the light of day in 1892. Florence just about makes the top 10 of names recorded by Matron, Elizabeth and variants being a clear leader, Anne and variants coming next, with Emily and Louisa doing well, but the only Nightingale on the list was christened Margaret. (In 1900 Florence was the top first name for girls, according to the *Guinness Book of Names* of 1974, only to have sunk without trace 25 years later.) FN's name may not have appeared in the minutes of the MAB but the ward blocks at Joyce Green were described as Pavilions, very much a Nightingale word, and the large windows were just what the bed-ridden Florence insisted on as essential for the room-bound invalid.

The remarkable thing about the ships' nurses is the speed with which they could be assembled when an epidemic struck and equally speedily dispersed when it was over. When he was first appointed Medical Superintendent (MS) Dr Ricketts handled nurse applications himself, writing in longhand in the official letterbook, the rice paper copies of which have survived. For instance, in August 1895, when there was a resurgence of smallpox: 'Madam, kindly meet me on Friday morning 23rd Inst. at 9.30 am punctually at the North Wharf, Coldharbour, Blackwall, bringing your testimonials with you'. That was to a Mrs Ellam, but things do not seem to have gone quite to plan for, 11 days later on 31 August, he wrote to her again: 'You seem to be taking some time in carrying out my instructions regarding your vaccination. As I informed you, it will be necessary for you to be done a third time before coming here, if the second vaccination is unsuccessful'.

Another letter said 'Take the train from Hackney, North London Railway, to Poplar, East India Dock Road. Coldharbour is a little more than half a mile from the station, I enclose a pass for the ambulance steamer, date it for the day on which you come'. (The line from Broad Street to Poplar was famous as the scene of the first murder on a British train in 1864.) Here is another letter, sorting out a familiar confusion of names, dated 21 August 1895: 'You speak in your letter of coming to Dartmouth, of course you must come to Dartford in Kent. Proceed by the SER from Cannon Street Station to Dartford, leaving at 5.38 pm, when you will find our conveyance waiting at Dartford Station. Otherwise you must take a cab.'

He was clearly irritated by delays, in view of the urgency brought about by the epidemic. '31 August; Madam, it is now a fortnight since I engaged your services. It is scandalously inconsiderate of you to cause me to keep the appointment open for you for that length of time and to no purpose. Obviously you could have made up your mind about it long before and you had no right to apply till you had done so. I return your papers.' In most of the letters he spells out the terms and conditions of service as they applied in 1895. 'Before coming here it will be necessary for you to be successfully re-vaccinated (or vaccinated three times unsuccessfully), I should therefore be glad if you would take steps at once to be vaccinated.' As regards duties: 'Nurses are required to take both day and night duty, the hours are from 7 o'clock until 7 o'clock, and leave of absence four days a month, with an annual holiday of four weeks to be taken when and if convenient to the administration of the hospital. Before leaving the hospital at any time, members of the staff are required to completely change their wearing apparel and take a bath. Indoor uniform is provided.'

Some people were appointed as assistant nurses, and their duties were to work in a ward under a charge nurse or otherwise if directed. The rough work was done by ward maids, who were required to take either day or night duty. Later, in 1902, Dr Ricketts was forced under stress of circumstance to accept unvaccinated nurses, on the understanding that they would be vaccinated immediately on arrival. Here it may be noted that six months since last vaccination was not a guarantee of immunity. '4 April 1902, Assistant Nurse Gregory who was transferred from the Northern Hospital on 15 March has developed smallpox. The disease was no doubt contracted here. Nurse Gregory was successfully re-vaccinated at the Northern Hospital in October 1901. Her attack is a very mild one.' There were 320 patients on the ships and at Long Reach Hospital at the time.

A sample of 85 nurses engaged during the 1901/02 epidemic shows that the average age of enrolment was 26.6 in the range 20 to 45 years. Many were by transfer from other institutes of the Board but some came from far afield and others from private nursing. They tended to come in pairs, including the Montague sisters, one of whom was a Florence, despite which they resigned after three months, thus ensuring that they did not forfeit their rail fare. Some said they would resign rather than go on night duty, though daytime must have been unpleasant enough. Others resigned rather than be transferred away, but these must have been the dedicated smallpox nurses.

For many, two to three months was quite enough, day or night, working with 'this loathsome disease in social isolation' to use Dr Ricketts' own words. As an example of long service we may take Mary Bennett who, according to the Nurses' Register, came to the ships on 31 August 1901 at the age of 35 as a charge nurse. She had started her nursing career in 1885 at Chichester, whence she moved to Liverpool, before coming down and joining the MAB nursing staff in July 1896 as a charge nurse at Gore Farm. Her duties at Long Reach cover the two years of the epidemic at the turn of the century before she was on her travels within the MAB, and we finally lose track of her when she went, yet again, to Gore Farm Hospital on 29 July 1910. Her conduct was described as good and her duties performed satisfactorily.

Charge Nurse Crowther, aged 38, joined at the same time, but her career was somewhat different, for she resigned on 27 November after less than three months, so forfeiting her train ticket fare from London. Before joining the ships she had done 10 years of private nursing, having trained at Charing Cross Hospital. Her general conduct at the hospital ships was described by Matron as fairly good, which is not quite how Dr Ricketts saw it for, on 22 October 1901, 'When passing through one of the ships I saw Charge Nurse Crowther behaving in an unseemly manner with one of the porters attending a delirious patient; the porter's name was Overshot and he has been reprimanded. [Male attendants were first employed in 1902.] A visitor to a dangerously ill patient was in the ward at the time.' Caught like that by the MS it is little wonder that Nancy Crowther resigned, but I am sure that, if it had been Matron's choice, she would have been more tolerant about this little indiscretion by a nurse whose work was described as satisfactory. There were nearly 200 patients in the hospital, so Matron was probably able to persuade Dr Ricketts to allow her to stay until a replacement had been appointed. At that time charge nurses were getting £38-£42 per annum, Matron £120 and Dr Ricketts had recently managed to get his salary put up from £400 to £700. In addition, nurses all got board and lodging, uniform and shoes, which Dr Ricketts reported as having unsatisfactory wearing qualities. But pity the poor ward maids, who were supplied with boots, for these were too heavy and the majority refused to wear them. Presumably nurses could use the hospital laundry, as in some of the letters he says 'washing is allowed'. Some maids as well as nurses came from private houses, for instance Florence Broderick, aged 18, had been a kitchen maid for nine months with Lady Flowers of Stanhope Gardens, Kensington and then second housemaid to Mrs Houlder of Ingress Abbey, Greenhithe, for one year and four months. This is longer than the eight months she spent as laundry maid on the ships or, to be precise, the shore establishment attached to the ships. Flora Bannister, aged 22, was tempted to become assistant nurse on 12 September 1901 in preference to being a nursery governess to a countess on Palma Major, but six months' smallpox nursing was enough for her. N. Ironer, aged 30, came down from Ripon in Yorkshire as a laundress, but she did not quite make the three months, so presumably lost the price of her third-class rail ticket, which 'will be refunded provided you do not retire before the expiration of three months'. As she left on 18 December 1901, it seems likely she could not bear the thought of spending Christmas in a floating smallpox hospital. She and Mary Mack, who came down from Ripon at about the same time, were probably friends, but Mary, who was engaged as a ward maid, lasted three years and was then transferred to the Park Hospital. Her conduct was said to be very good.

From 1904, with the epidemic over, the smallpox hospitals, including the new permanent Joyce Green Hospital, went into the doldrums, and the nursing staff was reduced to a skeleton. In 1914 Matron's Register of Staff was replaced by a Report Book, the ailing Dr Ricketts went as MS to the Park Hospital, to die there four years later, and Joyce Green was fully established as an overflow fever hospital.

Suddenly, with the advent of war and, unheard of prior to 1914, there were married nurses such as Assistant Nurse Tavender who, in 1915, was granted leave of absence from 10 to 12 December to go to see her husband who had returned from France. It must have been no surprise to Matron to receive a telegram stating that she was not returning on the 12th. The stresses of War are brought home vividly by ward maid Ada Fewell, who went absent having received a telegram saying her young man had been wounded, was home for eight days' leave and had been found on London Bridge suffering from loss of memory. The U-boat menace is highlighted by the Irish nurse who sent a certificate saying she would not be fit to return to the hospital for 14 days, when the real reason seems to have been that her mother was anxious about her crossing from Ireland owing to the war. It may be that the torpedoing of the *Lusitania* off the Irish coast was fresh in her memory. Alleged illness in members of their families may have been a contrived excuse for staying away while a relative or boyfriend was on leave from the trenches, like the ward maid who received a telegram to go home as her mother was ill. On her return a week later she said she could not submit a medical certificate as her mother had refused to have a doctor. Even in war, smoking could be a cause for dismissal, as with 2nd Assistant Nurse Millicent Graham. Responding to the noise emanating from Nurse Graham's cubicle, Assistant Matron Nash found four nurses there, the room thick with smoke, and there were said to be red-hot ashes on the carpet. Nurse Graham was dismissed the next day and the others let off with a caution.

The high level of absenteeism raised the question as to what they should be paid, an issue decided by a sub-committee of the Board called the Interim Visitors. On 20 May 1916 they had to decide on five nurses and four maids who had been reported; they declared *inter alia* that a brother on leave from the front was not a sufficient excuse for Assistant Nurse Marlow to be paid for her two days' absence.

Finally, pity Assistant Nurse Class II Annie Victoria Stains who, on 6 August 1915, was reported for smoking in her bedroom, and also that she had visited the Bull Hotel in Dartford with a soldier who had previously been a patient in the hospital. The Medical Superintendent sent for her parents to fetch her away and she left the hospital on 11 August. Which crime, one wonders, was the more heinous: smoking in her bedroom or drinking with a soldier? Maybe she joined the Queen Alexandra's Imperial Nursing Service (QA's), as did a steady stream of nurses.

The power of the MS to hand out instant dismissal was waning for as far back as 1912 the MAB was disturbed by the instant dismissal powers of the MS. It was pointed out that suspension of an officer by a Medical Superintendent was not final and was liable to reversal by the Managers. If the suspended person was required to leave the institution, and the Managers subsequently removed the suspension, compensation for expenses might be payable. They stressed that, with female staff, the objections to sudden turning out-of-doors were exceptionally strong, and that on the whole they discountenanced the procedure of requiring suspended persons of either sex to leave the institution. The reduced powers of the MS did not help Nurse de Gruchy who, in December 1915, was suspended by the MS but dismissed following instruction from the Chairman of the Hospitals Committee. Her crime? A cup of tea in the kitchen of Ward 15A, having left ward 15B to take down a newspaper, or so she said.

It is unfair perhaps to the memory of Medical Superintendents to think of them as little more than hirers and firers. On 3 September 1901, at the beginning of a major outbreak, Dr Ricketts wrote of his staff 'Great pressure has been thrown on the staff in consequence of this outbreak, the nursing staff particularly has been much overworked, largely on account of the severity of the cases. The old nurses whom you had in your service have been of the greatest possible assistance and it has been a source of the greatest regret to me that this number was not greater. They have worked ceaselessly and ungrudgingly. The domestic staff has also been willingly overworked.' Fortunately for the service he quickly got 15 nurses, three laundry maids and seven ward maids transferred from other MAB hospitals. As noted previously, male attendants were employed from 1902, before which Dr Ricketts had to use porters as male attendants for delirious patients, the particular problem being the ease with which they could jump overboard from the *Castalia*. He recommended the erection of a male staff hut to accommodate 12 men. It is not clear when qualified male nurses were first employed, but in 1913 Dr Ricketts sought replacement of two from the Male Nurses' Association.

The smallpox hospital ships' only Matron was Miss Helen Wacher, who was in post from the start in 1884, and continued on shore at the River Hospitals till 1916. A few years ago I had the opportunity to talk to someone whose memory went back to the First World War, and he could just remember her somewhat unusual name, which he said was pronounced to rhyme with acacia. Fortunately, photos of her and her staff survive, and enable us to see a large, matronly figure struggling to achieve a wasp waist like the bevy of beauty around her. In one of these pictures there is a nice touch, for she has a small black puppy on her lap, though there is no evidence that dogs were allowed in a smallpox hospital without let or hindrance. We do not know her age, for she omitted details of herself in the Staff Register, but she retired, probably from ill-health, in 1916 after 32 years of intermittent service at the River Hospitals. Intermittent because, in keeping with the normal practice of the MAB, she was transferred from time to time to other of the Board's institutions when there was little or no smallpox about. But if she was away for months at a time, delegation was inevitable, and before 1901 this was usually to Miss Louisa Barton, who was not a trained nurse at all, but a housekeeper or head needlewoman. Probably, in the absence of an epidemic, her duties and Miss Wacher's were not all that different, as judged by Dr Ricketts' report of 29 May 1900: 'Miss Wacher has been absent at the Grove Hospital since 16 June 1899. Before that, from 26 May 1898 she was engaged in supervising the work at the Managers' Needle Rooms in the Borough'. During nearly the whole of that time her duties devolved on Assistant Matron Barton, whose work he praised to the skies, and then came the key sentence: 'I think Miss Barton deserves well of the Managers and I trust the Hospital Sub-Committee will see their way to recommending that she be suitably recompensed'. The Board got the message and Miss Barton £30 and, while they were about it, they threw in £52 10s for Miss Wacher.

However, by November doubts were arising as to Miss Barton's suitability as Matron. 'Miss Barton is a very valuable officer' wrote Dr Ricketts 'and has done excellent service; but she was promoted to her present office from the domestic staff, she is ignorant of nursing matters and cannot be expected to exercise adequate control over the nurses. I think the difficulty would be best met by making Miss Barton housekeeper, a position she already occupies in practice and by appointing a trained Assistant Matron.' And so it came about that, on 7 October 1901, a Miss Cottrill was transferred from the South Eastern Hospital to the River Hospitals and the 'exceedingly painstaking and conscientious' Miss Barton was regraded Housekeeper at a salary drop of £10 per year. Once again Dr Ricketts put in a good word for her and the MAB sweetened her demotion pill to the tune of £20.

Miss Cottrill's appointment was in the nick of time, for the country's last major outbreak of smallpox had just started. As for Miss Barton, she stayed on as Housekeeper at the River Hospitals till 1908 when, at the age of 53, she was superannuated under the 1896 Act for an undisclosed allowance, her appeal for more being turned down by the MAB. As for Miss Wacher, her notice of resignation was referred to the Board on 27 May 1916, but not until 14 October do they record that Miss N. H. Thorpe, First Assitant Matron Brook Hospital, was promoted to be a Matron in the infectious hospital service at a scaled rate of salary 'and that until further orders her service be allocated to the River Hospitals and Ambulance Service', a title which stresses the importance of the nurses on the ambulance steamers and at South Wharf. Thus the MAB retained the right to move her around as they had done with Miss Wacher, but in the event she spent the next 15 years at Joyce Green, retiring in the summer of 1929, leaving as her memorial a bird bath and a Wendy statuette. Dr Marsden, the Assistant MS, remembered her as a nice, round, comfortable-looking old lady known as Queen Victoria.

When Matron Thorpe arrived she had her hands full with outbreaks of scarlet fever and diphtheria, followed by the influenza pandemic which greeted the end of the war, and was said to have killed more people than were killed in the trenches. The scale of staff sickness was impressive for, during 1920, Dr Cameron reported that 55 of the staff had contracted scarlet fever and 14 diphtheria. In November 1921, 30 nurses and ward maids were suffering from scarlet fever and three from diphtheria. Apart from staff sickness, the two main problems facing Miss Thorpe were the registration of trained nurses and the employment of institution (agency) nurses, of which they had 133 at the beginning of 1922. Over 60 years later we seem to be no nearer solving the problem. Then as now agency nurses cost more, two guineas per week in 1907 according to Dr Ricketts, whereas an MAB nurse was paid £30-£40 pa depending on grade.

When Miss Thorpe retired there were 179 cases of the mild form of smallpox in Joyce Green, so her successor, Miss Morris, had the main burden of coping with the nursing aspects of this variola minor or alastrim outbreak which, as it happens, was the first and last time that Joyce Green Hospital was intensively used for the nursing of smallpox. In Miss Thorpe's last report, dated 24 October 1928, was an entry that Staff Nurse Eva P. H. Emery and Kitchen Assistant Class 1, Constance Ashby, were given notice owing to impending marriage. Nevertheless, after the 1914/18 war the MAB had not been able to put the clock back completely, for Minutes such as this one dated July 1923 appeared from time to time: 'Employment of married women; 18 retained in the Board's service, notwithstanding the fact that they were married women'.

Miss Thorpe's successor was of a different type, but the MS, Dr Cameron, thought a lot of her for after he retired in 1937, he married her. She was called Daisy because she used to ride round the outer road on a bicycle — made for one presumably. It would have been more than his life was worth for Dr Cameron to be seen fraternising with her for, in March 1930, a trip round the outer road after a dance had been the downfall of two Ward Sisters and a Doctor, and Dr Cameron was the executioner. 'The Sisters did not return to their rooms until 12.45 am' he wrote 'the dance having ceased at 11.45 pm. The Sisters were allowed to resign and left the next day as well as Dr Gilsenan.' There were over 1,000 smallpox patients in the hospital, so a dance with visitors from the outside was a surprise, but even more of a surprise is the fact that he could dispose of the services of two Sisters when the hospital was so busy.

Miss Morris' written record of her term of office ends in 1933; then there is a fleeting glimpse of her in March 1935 when Dr Cameron reported that she was off duty with laryngitis and bronchitis. She retired one year after Dr Cameron in 1937 and her successor, Miss Hyde, came on 1 October — the same day as Dr Mitman took over as MS, so she was probably a protegé of his, and a formidable pair they must have made.

Hospital Ships.

18

The following Nurses have leave of absence this day :—

(55)

from   to

Hospital Ships, leave of absence list.

ABOVE: Matron's cabin on the *Endymion*, full of Victorian bric-a-brac and a prize-winning aspidistra.
BELOW: Matron Wacher with black puppy on lap and nurses, on Long Reach tennis court, c1902. Note the wasp waists.

ABOVE: Assistant Matron, Louisa Barton, on Long Reach tennis court with the same carpet but different nurses and dog, probably in 1901, the year Miss Barton was demoted to housekeeper. The tennis court was built by Alfred Watts and Wm Fitchett in 1895. BELOW: Nurses, patients and Dr A. H. Haddow probably on the same day in 1915, outside 12 Block, Joyce Green Hospital. Pince-nez must have been in fashion.

ABOVE: Nurses and patients at Joyce Green in 1915. BELOW: Nurses' sitting room, Joyce Green Hospital. The arum lilies are probably the photographer's props. Gas lights with opaque globes over mantles mean this picture was taken before 1926.

Smallpox distribution map, 1902. Note the contrast between the City and massively infected Stepney.

68

PATIENTS

'A tender plant so young and fair
Nipped in the bud by cruel disease
Called to that heavenly home above
To flower in beauty and in love.'
Epitaph on tombstone in Darenth Asylum Cemetery.

By good fortune the notes of nearly all the smallpox patients who attended the ships and River Hospitals have survived, and from these a range of facts can be gleaned. For instance, in 1901, out of 300 patients, 44 were labourers and 50 from a wide range of occupations including:
Polishers, trimmers, clickers and blowers,
Grinders of stone and sellers of flowers,
Gilders of pictures and banders of gloves,
Makers of sacks and dispensers of drugs,
Trooper, trimmer, traveller, porter,
Mother, father, son and daughter.
Dressers of skins and fryers of fish,
They all went down to the Ships at Long Reach.
This makes an interesting comparison with the list of 63 patients compiled by Dr R. A. Birdwood in 1891, the first Medical Superintendent of the Floating Hospitals, as they were then called. The main purpose of the list was an attempt to assess whether the size of the vaccination scar was related to the degree of immunity conferred, but Dr Birdwood included their occupation, most of the patients being dock workers of one sort or another. There was one law student and one steward from the SS *Cadiz*, who had been exposed to smallpox at Lisbon about two weeks before the ship arrived in London. Why the dockers had disappeared from the 1901 list is not clear, but perhaps they were listed under 'labourer', or was it simply that the disease had spread out from the docks where it presumably originated? A glance at the map shows a high concentration of patients in Stepney and a remarkable absence in the neighbouring City of London. Clustering of cases is very characteristic of smallpox and is in marked contrast to the diffuse spread of scarlet fever. In 1891 Dr Birdwood reported on just such a cluster of 10 cases and, because of the two-week incubation period, successive generations could be recognised. The outbreak started with a dock labourer. Two weeks later his brother, a fellow lodger and the potman at a local pub sickened. Another two weeks later and the potman's wife, a visitor and two more lodgers fell ill. Finally on 2 May, seven weeks after the dock labourer fell ill, the mother of one of the ill lodgers who had visited her sick child was struck down. Were it not for the potman who recognised the nature of the disease the outbreak might have spread further. The final twist was that the man who came to disinfect the house himself fell ill with smallpox.

At the end of 1891 there was an outbreak of smallpox among the mainly Swiss waiters at the Helvetia Club, seven people in all being brought down to the ships. John Sykes, the Medical Officer of Health for St Pancras who made enquiries in London, wrote in despair that 'the statements made are as numerous as the persons that made them and are extremely contradictory, the truth is still lying at the bottom of a very deep well. I very strongly suspect that an unrecognised case of smallpox has been stalking about in the guise of a waiter.'

Forty people including the Swiss waiters lived at 107 Charlotte Street, so a large cluster of cases could be expected were it not that the Vaccination Officer, a lay official, acted promptly, and the Public Vaccinator, a medical man, visited the house on the evening of 5 January 1892 at 9.30 pm and revaccinated all the occupants. One of the Swiss waiters sent a thank you letter to Dr Birdwood; 'I am very much obliged to you, Sir, I only wish I could write to you in my own language, I could do it better, but I know you will understand me. Dear sir I am exceedingly sorry to trouble you with a favour I am obliged to ask you. Would you have the kindness and send me, at the Helvetia Club, a certificate concerning the date on which I fell ill, also the date on which I left the hospital, and oblige your obedient servant, Julius Freudiger.'

A final example of clustering is of eight cases in three families — Smith (2), Williams (3), Ivanhoe (3) — living at 53 Euston Street, who fell ill between 27 February and 2 April, four in mid-March and three at the beginning of April, their ages ranging from 24 years to seven days. This outbreak was prolonged because two people, one being the 24-year-old mother, were first diagnosed as chickenpox at New Cross Hospital. Two outside contact cases appeared on 19 March, John Morris, 34, proprietor of the local pub, and on 2 April, Eliza Edwards, 35, of Prospect Terrace, who washed the linen of one of the inhabitants of 53 Euston Street, both ideal foci from which new clusters develop.

A touching family history is related by Mrs Newstead of Dartford in 1988. Her grandparents were married on Xmas Day 1901. He, Fred Letchford, was admitted with smallpox in January 1902, leaving his new bride isolated at home in Old Bexley. There she was alone for nearly three weeks, her supplies being left at the door. Happily he recovered and brought window frames etc, from Dartford to Joyce Green for the new hospital on his horse and cart, down the narrow Joyce Green Lane.

In the outbreak of mild smallpox (variola minor) which lasted from 1928 to 1934, the type of patient had changed again. The majority were children and unvaccinated, 82% in one sample of 127 from consecutive admissions in 1930. These unvaccinated children accounted for nearly all the patients under the age of 30, 52 being under the age of 14, so clearly the vaccination service had collapsed during the 1914/18 war. As regards the adults, there were 18 housewives, the next largest group being the unemployed with 10, an indication perhaps that the slump in the 1930s was beginning. The occupations of those who were gainfully employed reflect the changing pattern of trade and industry and include tobacco shipper, peanut blancher, gramophone dealer, plywood manufacturer and motor driver, but miscellaneous small trades are well represented, including makers of chairs, caps and boats. If the outbreak had been the severe type of smallpox (variola major) the mortality would indeed have been formidable, whereas it was less than 1%. Over 13,500 patients with smallpox passed through the River Hospitals and nearly all of them were seen by Dr J. Pickford Marsden. His review of them published in 1936 is probably the best account of variola minor that there is.

So far as we can judge from the notes, the working man and his family from London were a most uncomplaining group of people, partly perhaps through illiteracy, for thank you and other letters are usually the work of professional letter-writers with their beautiful Victorian copperplate. The thank you letters that have survived are prior to 1892, after which they were not inserted in the notes. The most telling letter was from a docker: 'Dear Docktor Birdwood, Just a line to let you know that i come home all wright on Saturday thanking you very much indeed for the kindness i received while i was in the Hospital. And all the nurses for the kindness I received Nurse Stone, Nurse Allen, Nurse Kirbey thanking them very much indeed, hoping to see them very shortly I might come down to Dartford on Sunday week at the Railway Station. I should like to see the Docktor Because he is a Gentleman in every inch of him. I remains yours very truly, Richard Lyttleton'.

Next is a typical thank you letter from 1891, sent by a Mr Mason who was a dock official. The beautiful copperplate handwriting and formal style suggest the work of a letterwriter. 'Sir I feel I should be neglecting a duty and more particularly the dictates of my heart were I to allow the occasion of my dear wife's return to pass, without asking you to accept my heartfelt gratitude for the great kindness extended to her whilst she was under your care at Long Reach'. A search through the smallpox notes showed that two other people. Archibald Trumble, aged 20, and Mabel Trumble, aged 14, were admitted from the same address at about the same time.

Some letters from patients are in response to an inquiry; this one is from a father about his daughter. 'Dear Sir, I have to thank you for kind letter respecting my daughter M. Barry who arrive here [there] safely with severe attack of smallpox. We hope and trust she will get over it, please God.' He explained that she had not been vaccinated at birth because she was a delicate child. He did not know how she came to be infected for she had not been near anyone who had spots on them. He continued 'I might say my youngest child, five years old, was just getting over an attack of measles when she took ill. In conclusion I must say the W C has not the continuse supply of water and also there is a nasty smelling drain in the kitchen. Again thanking you for your kind letter, I remain her sorrowful father.' As Dr Birdwood would have noted, the clue to the mystery lies in the brother's attack of so-called measles, for as Avicenna (980-1037) first noted, the physical signs of measles can be nearly the same as those of smallpox. Happily, Mary Barry recovered, but less happily she must have been left with a pock-marked face for her smallpox was described as severe vesicular. She was admitted to the ships on 25 March and discharged on 16 May, and was put on a sick diet with beef tea.

Ellen Chapman left an account of the comings and goings in a small East End sweat shop, such as that from which Charlie Chaplin's mother in the 1890s earned a precarious living sewing blouses at 1s 6d a dozen. Ellen arrived at the hospital ships on 1 April 1888, and her story is of particular interest, as it was written down verbatim. 'Daniel Devonport living at Bow had smallpox very slight eight weeks ago. Whilst he had it he stopped two nights at his young womans, Miss Daniels — they have married since. A little girl living at Miss Daniels house Lizzie Kelly had it very slight. A little boy two and a half years old unvaccinated living in same house died of smallpox about 13 Feb. The boy and girl were ill together. Their half sister Ada Miller came to 3 Ida Street a week after the boy died. Mrs. Angel living at 3 Ida Street had smallpox and she was bad (three weeks yesterday 31 Mar). Patient went to 3 Ida Street daily for her work. Ada Miller makes baby robes with Miss Bogues at 3 Ida Street. Patient also makes baby robes and takes the work home.'

Here is how Dr Ricketts responded to a complaint from a 38-year-old milliner. He noted that, during her sojourn in hospital, Miss Howell appeared happy and contented and made no complaint at any time. 'On the contrary I am informed by the nurses that she repeatedly expressed her gratitude and repeatedly stated she had been very happy.' He continues 'With regard to the point about patients rising when the doctor enters the ward, I need only say that this is the usual custom in hospitals and as to the complaint about early rising I may point out that our rule required convalescent patients to be up by 7 am in order to allow the day nurses, who come on duty at that hour, to get on with the ward work. I have had patients here of all classes and I have not found among them any objection to conform to the rules which are not very strict. Miss Howell's first complaint is that the treatment was inadequate, and I fancy that the basis of her dissatisfaction lies in the fact that her face has been marked by the disease so as to interfere with her following her occupation as a milliner. This receives support from a letter I enclose, which I happened to have received from her mother.' Dr Ricketts pointed out that 'Miss Howell had been vaccinated unsuccessfully in infancy and that she had a severe attack of smallpox accompanied by a troublesome eruption of boils on the face. There is always a percentage of these in which there is more or less scarring and it was Miss Howell's misfortune to come in this category. I am sorry for her but it could not be helped' — a resigned recognition that treatment at best was only palliative.

A complaint about delay of notification gives an interesting glimpse of the postal services of 1895. 'The patient arrived here on the afternoon of 25 December and the first post leaving here after that was 6 pm on the 26th so the notice could not be delivered in London before this morning 27 December' — quick by our standards.

Most smallpox patients who died were buried in the hospital cemeteries, either at Darenth Asylum or after 1902 at Joyce Green itself. Occasionally relatives wished to take the body away. On one occasion Dr Ricketts had to point out that there would be problems about moving a body to Yorkshire unless it was enclosed in a leaden shell, hermetically sealed. 'I do not suppose that otherwise the railway company or the health authorities would sanction the removal. The railway difficulty would be avoided by taking the body by road. Such a long journey would take two or three days and be very expensive and there would be a risk of meeting with difficulties en route on account of the nature of your brother's illness. You will see that it will be a very troublesome and expensive business to carry out your wish and there is sure to be considerable delay. I should strongly therefore advise you to allow the funeral to take place in our private cemetery here.'

The cemetery record book at Darenth has disappeared, but a few of those buried were given headstones enabling us to confirm that the smallpox victims were buried there alongside the patients of the Asylum and an occasional member of staff. The stones were put there by relatives who could afford it, with or without the help of their employers. One such was Ebenezer Palmer of the Africa Direct Telegraph Company, Accra who, having survived the hazards of the white man's grave, had the misfortune to arrive home at the height of an epidemic and pick up the infection soon after arrival. The epitaph to 43 year old Walter John Robinson has a peculiar misprint:—

'DAY BY DAY WE ALL DO MISS HIM
WORDS WOULD FAIL OUR LOSS TO TELL
BUT WE HOPE IN HEAVEN TO MET HIH
EVERMORE WITH HIH TO DWELL.'

Perhaps the stonemason thought 'HIH' stood for the deity or a guardian angel. Annie Timm, whose epitaph is quoted at the head of the chapter, was the 26-year-old wife of a policeman who lived in Bishopsgate Without in the City. She had been vaccinated in infancy and was a good example of the evidence, by then conclusive to medical experts, that vaccination in infancy did not convey life long immunity as Jenner had hoped. Increasingly they demanded revaccination and indeed people who worked with smallpox could expect to be vaccinated about every two years.

The Darenth Asylum Cemetery was well kept up to 1988 and daffodils still flower on Annie Timms' grave. Joyce Green Cemetery on the other hand is overgrown and vandalised, but the record book is complete and gives precise location of the burials. When the cemetery opened in February 1902 the epidemic was at its highest, and burials were up to 10 to a grave, but perhaps half of those would be small children. After 1902 the cemetery was little used, and after 1907 some of the burials were fever patients, possibly children of parents in London who could not afford to remove the body for burial elsewhere. In 1943 Mr Golden, the Steward, carried out a survey of memorials in Joyce Green Cemetery and found about 40 of one sort or another. A few had head and kerb stones, some just headstones or kerbstones and others a simple cross. Grave number 66 had a stone commemorating Harry Smith, aged 36, even though eight other bodies were buried there, including Lily Smith, aged four months, who might have been his daughter.

After the 1914/18 war, smallpox showed a resurgence, and Nurse Chapman was one of 42 deaths in 1922 — a particularly sad case because, being a nurse, she should have been protected by revaccination. In severe epidemics the mortality rate might be as high as 25% at the beginning when the worst cases usually appeared, but overall the death rate at Long Reach was 13%.

For the majority of patients who went home there was a standard bathing routine before discharge — day 1 Condy's bath, day 2 soap and water bath, day 3 Sanitas bath, and if you were lucky you went back in your own clothes. Because of the workhouse background, clothes tended to be destroyed and replaced, but attitudes had changed as many of the patients were not paupers, and Dr Ricketts refused to destroy any, however ragged, and here he crossed swords with Dr Thompson of Gore Farm Convalescent Hospital. Another problem was that for many, their clothes had been left behind in London before they embarked on the ambulance steamers. Doubtless there were some, perhaps many, especially vagrants, who would have been only too happy to receive a new set of clothing in place of their old rags.

Nowadays it is hard to conceive of the pressure on the newly opened Joyce Green Cemetery, but in March 1902 there were 200 deaths and it is not hard to see why Dr Ricketts had estimated that 20 grave diggers would need to be employed during an epidemic, or why they buried them at up to 10 in one grave. The burials were obviously quite simple, and Dr Ricketts mentions straw and charcoal to absorb the juices, so presumably the coffins were reused. Local coffin-makers would have been hard-pushed to provide 200 new coffins a month. These were the pressures which caused the MAB to consider building a crematorium at Joyce Green. The proposal was turned down; possibly it was before its time and there were also religious objections. In 1902 all deaths were at Long Reach or on the hospital ships, so it would have been a long, slow, two-mile trek to pull the biers along Marsh Street and around the back of the half-built Joyce Green. No-one knows how many horses were needed. Once Joyce Green was built, the journey was much shorter, but Dr Ricketts was worried that visitors to the hospital would be met by a procession of mortuary biers leaving by the same gate.

In the event, that did not arise because, by the time Joyce Green opened at the end of 1903, the epidemic was over and deaths were few. Not until 1922 was there another epidemic and then only a minor one in numbers, and nothing like as severe. Of the 42 deaths, let us remember Ethel Clara Chapman, whose epitaph speaks for them all. She was both nurse and patient — nurse at the Poplar Institution, where she contracted the disease, and patient in Long Reach Hospital, where she died on 7 November 1922 at the age of 24. The simple epitaph on her tombstone reads 'To live in the hearts we leave behind is not to die.'

ABOVE: Darenth Asylum, in whose grounds the smallpox story began in 1881, at closure in 1988. View from cemetery. (A) CENTRE: The cemetery in 1989, neglected once the asylum closed. Ebenezer Palmer's tombstone is in the centre (A) and LEFT: in close-up. (A) BELOW: Three French soldiers carved their names in brick on the wall of 11a ward, Joyce Green. (A) OPPOSITE ABOVE: Joyce Green patient's ironing room. In 1927 there were 50,000 items of clothing in stock, many old-fashioned like the 3,000 pinafores. In 1931 Dr Cameron hoped they could be suitably converted. BELOW: Spring time in a fever ward at Joyce Green, c1920

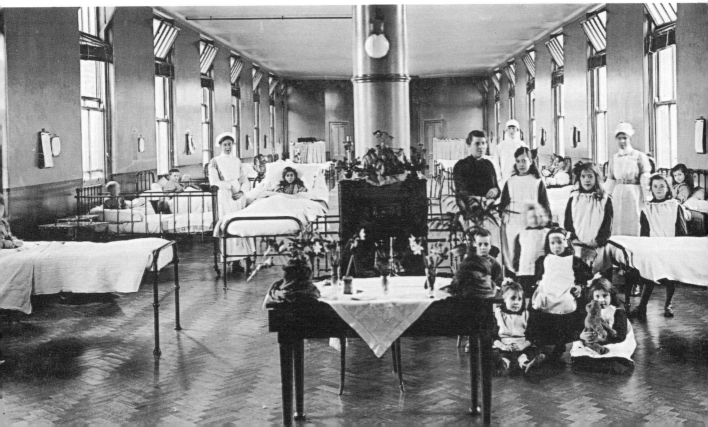

ABOVE: This is almost certainly Dr Ricketts' wife — is it her standing in the photograph of The Warren? The house was demolished and replaced in 1935. A former occupant was Sir Erasmus Wilson FRCS, who brought Cleopatra's Needle to London. BELOW: The Warren, Greenhithe where Dr Ricketts and family lived till 1898. He labelled the negative of this photo 'the Women'.

DR RICKETTS

'For I am a man under authority, having soldiers under me; and I say to this man, Go, and he goeth; and to another, Come, and he cometh; and to my servant, Do this, and he doeth it.'

Centurion in *Matthew* Chap 8, v9.

The Medical Superintendents (MS) of the MAB were powerful people, but whether this was acquired over the years or whether it was written into their contract, if indeed they had one, is not clear. The policy of the MAB seems to have been to move their Medical Superintendents around and Dr R. A. Birdwood, the first MS on the ships, was no exception, for in 1892 he was transferred to the Eastern Fever Hospital. He was replaced by a young man of 27, Thomas Frank Ricketts who, though he did not know it at the time, was to stay for 22 years and become the leading smallpox expert of the day, and perhaps even of all time.

Dr Ricketts came from Frocester in Gloucestershire, less than 10 miles from Berkeley, so Edward Jenner, the pioneer of vaccination, may well have been one of his boyhood heroes, and an important influence in his choice of career. He came to the ships as MS only three years after medical qualification, and one year after getting his London MD, to gold medal standard. His smallpox apprenticeship was served a few miles up the road at Gore Farm Hospital, so he came to the Hospital Ships relatively inexperienced but, to be made Superintendent at the age of 27, he must have stood head and shoulders above the other Assistant Medical Officers.

But in those days it is to be supposed that few medical men with greater experience of smallpox were available to the MAB and, in choosing Ricketts, young though he was, they backed a winner. He was married too, but the MAB's prejudice against married Medical Superintendents was to come later, by 1914 perhaps, when his successor was the asthmatic bachelor, Dr A. F. Cameron.

Fifty years after Dr Ricketts' death his successors still accorded him a near godlike infallibility in the diagnosis of smallpox, and it was only gradually that the verdict of the electron microscope replaced the verdict of the full clinical examination as practised and taught by Ricketts. This reverence was well expressed by Dr J. Pickford Marsden in 1948, when he wrote of 'Ricketts to whom on matters pertaining to smallpox the present writer looks as the ultimate authority.' The same reverential admiration was brought out in his obituary notice in the *British Medical Journal* in February 1918: 'What made his diagnosis unchallengeable was that he brought to his work a scientific mind of the finest calibre which made work look easy. The extreme difficulty of making a correct diagnosis of every one of many thousands of cases presented as smallpox is a commonplace. Dr Ricketts' skill was almost uncanny, his work in this field was brilliant and conducted with gentle decision and modesty.' They concluded by saying that 'he was admired as a mastermind, respected for his courage and commonsense, attractive by reason of his sense of humour and correct opinions, and loved as a friend'. Unfortunately the written record he left behind him in the form of letters, copies of which have survived in the hospital, and reports to the MAB, leave no room for his sense of humour, but stress his role as a disciplinarian.

One of his earlier acts was to prohibit members of the staff attending functions in the neighbourhood, and he was forced to cancel leave to prevent a planned attendance at a dance in Dartford. This had arisen after an earlier incident in Dr Birdwood's time, when it was alleged that members of the ships' staff had conveyed smallpox to Erith.

It must have been incidents such as this that prompted him to write that social isolation on the ships was excessive. We may be sure that he felt this social isolation as much as the staff who were forced to stay aboard instead of having a kick-up. One way around this 'confinement to barracks' was to plead illness in themselves or in a member of their family. But in June 1895 the idea backfired, one domestic sending a doctor's certificate that she was unfit to return to duty. 'But I found that on the day following that on which she should have returned to duty she was well enough to spend the day at Rosherville Gardens'. Another girl, who also went to Rosherville Gardens, got special leave by presenting to the Matron a telegram summoning her to see her sister who was dangerously ill. Dr Ricketts recommended that 'in these cases the circumstances under which the resignations took place should be entered in their testimonials'. Usually the reason for resigning was not entered in the testimonial, so many people quickly resigned rather than risk a 'dismissed' on their sheet. Rosherville Gardens, which were situated at the east end of the Parish of Northfleet, were described as of surpassing beauty, and the remains of the pier and promenade can still be seen. It was still fashionable at the time — perhaps the Prince of Wales and Lily Langtry were there the very day the domestics took french leave.

The Prince and other people of fashion must often have passed those hulks moored in Long Reach, but if ever they were moved to comment it is not recorded. Typhoid, not smallpox, was the Royal disease of the 19th century; if any Royals *had* come out in spots, the ships might well have described themselves as under Royal patronage. Perhaps, though, Royalty would have been the exception to the rule that all patients with smallpox in the MAB area should be brought down to Long Reach.

To celebrate the peace in the Crimean War on 6 January 1902 two boatmen and a porter broke hospital bounds and rowed over to celebrate in Purfleet. Dr Ricketts must have viewed this transgression seriously, for it blew sky-high the rule that no member of staff should leave the hospital without first having a bath and changing his or her clothes; what is more there were over 300 patients, half of them in the newly opened Long Reach Hospital. The men's punishment was suspension, which was lenient by the standards of the time.

Dr Ricketts' pursuit of diagnostic perfection sometimes brought him into conflict with his professional elders and betters. In April 1899, after seven years as MS of the Hospital Ships, but still only aged 35, he wrote 'It is unpleasant to have to override violently the deliberate opinion of a certifier, who may be a medical officer of health or a physician of standing, perhaps with experience of smallpox'. This was in response to a forceful attack on him by three experienced physicians. He rightly stressed how important it was that a case which was not smallpox should never be sent down to the ships 'and that if such a case is unfortunately sent the true nature of the disease shall be recognised at the earliest moment in order that proper precautions may be taken to prevent the patient getting smallpox'. He then gave figures to demonstrate the success of his policy. In 1893, of 2,360 cases of smallpox sent to the ships, 72 were found to be not suffering from smallpox. By 1895 he had reduced the figure to five out of 934.

In January 1899, a year in which there were only five patients treated in the ships, he took time to consider the future, and made an accurate forecast of the next epidemic. 'From the maximum in 1884 to that in 1893 is a cycle of nine years with yearly admissions falling through five years and rising through four. At the present time it appears to have touched bottom of another cycle. Epidemics of smallpox came in similar cycles before the year 1884, but an unusual feature of the 1884/1893 cycle was its length. I think these facts justify us in expecting in the next few years, smallpox will be more rife in London than it has been recently. And further we ought to assume that you will have to deal with a comparatively large number of patients within four years from 1898.'

He pointed out that London was not as well vaccinated as it had been for many years and, in consequence of the Vaccination Act of 1898 relaxing the compulsory rule, it would in a few years' time be classed as a town badly protected from the disease. The prospect of larger numbers of smallpox cases than in the recent past led him to look with some anxiety on the fact that the projected Joyce Green Smallpox Hospital was not then even commenced. He pointed out the unsuitability of a floating hospital in the middle of the river Thames, where it was highly likely to be involved in a serious collision, and he concluded 'I have shown you in another report, a hospital of this peculiar nature is for hygienic reasons singularly ill-adapted to the treatment of any infectious disease and especially to the treatment of smallpox.' He was probably referring to the discharge of raw sewage from the ships into the river, a small but important contribution to a river which, in 1899, was so grossly contaminated as to be devoid of life.

Still in 1899, he found time to write a long letter complaining that his salary was less than that of a Medical Superintendent at a fever hospital who, in 1898, had had his raised to £700 as a maximum, leaving him with £400, the same as he had received for the last six and a half years. He said that he was entirely willing to transfer his services to a fever hospital now but 'other things being equal I would prefer to remain here and I understand that you think that would be in the managers' interests', a clear indication of his dedication to his chosen career as a smallpox expert. The letter had the desired effect. At their November meeting the Finance Committee made the necessary adjustment, for they must have known that he was irreplaceable.

Five years previously he had put in a good word for the pockets of his Assistant Medical Officers. He pointed out that their responsibility was much greater on the ships than at a fever hospital. 'It has to be borne in mind' he wrote 'that a smallpox hospital is peculiarly under the eye of the public, and any error is liable to be the subject of public comment. Besides there being extra responsibility, you will see that the disadvantages of service here are much greater than those attached to service in a fever hospital, in as much as the work is more monotonous, the disease treated is loathsome, and the social isolation is excessive. The result is, as I have found, that suitable men are difficult to obtain.' Perhaps the wonder is that staff of any grade, doctors, nurses or ward maids could be obtained so seemingly easily.

A rise in salary may have been hard to come by unless one pestered Management, but tax returns were simple. 'To the Surveyor of Taxes Woolwich. In reply to your letter of yesterday (24 January 1898) in which you inquire how I arrive at the sum of £389 8s 0d which I gave as the amount of my income which was formerly £400. There is now deducted the amount of £10 12s 0d under the (Poor Law Officers) Superannuation Act. The amount I now actually receive annually is therefore £389 8s 0d. T. F. Ricketts'. The effect of the 1896 Act led to complaints by the crews of the Ambulance Steamers that their weekly wage packets had been reduced.

Previously those who left after a period of service went penniless unless the Board felt that they could make them an *ex gratia* superannuation allowance, as they did in February 1896 to James Dixon, late mate on the ambulance steamboats. He got £21 4s per annum, being 12/60 of his wages and emoluments.

In 1898 Dr Ricketts and his family moved to Southfield House from their home in Greenhithe in anticipation of the building of Joyce Green Hospital. Their rent was £30 per annum and Dr Ricketts optimistically presumed that the Board would make the necessary alterations and repairs. Southfield House, which was built in 1879, came to the MAB when they purchased the land on which Joyce Green Hospital was built. The entrance is directly opposite that of the cemetery, something they were probably not aware of in 1898, four years before it opened.

Dr Ricketts may have been hard on malefactors, but he argued the case cogently for those who, in his opinion, were being scurvily treated by the Board. Of engineer Bamford, 1 September 1896: 'You will remember that the engineer has been warded, and that at the last meeting of the Committee it was decided that his wages should be paid in full for another fortnight, and that subsequently he should go on half pay if his illness continues. After the date of this Committee meeting he had a slight relapse and was in consequence ill a week longer than I anticipated. He therefore received half pay for one week. The man has since spoken to me about this and thinks he is rather hardly used. I quite agree with him, he is the first officer in whose case this rule as to half pay has been applied. While he has been ill he has still superintended his department from his bed, and he is, I think, about the hardest worked man in the hospital.' Anything Florence Nightingale could do from her bed he could do too!

During epidemic times Dr Ricketts' mind was kept fully occupied with his patients, but in between he could apply himself to other matters with enthusiasm, and in 1899 he gave detailed specifications on the construction of a delirious ward on the *Castalia*.
'1. All outside windows, including window of WC to be barred outside.
2. The lower sash of each window to have a moveable grating fixed to it. This should be of such a nature as to prevent a patient breaking the glass and cutting himself. The grating should be fixed onto the sash frame so that it raises with the sash and fixed in such a manner eg with screws and fly nuts, that it can be removed from the window to be cleaned. The window of the WC and the observation window to be treated in the same way.
3. The entrance door from the ward should be glazed in the upper half, the glass to be protected with grating on the inner side as above described.
4. The door of the water closet should have fastenings designed to prevent a patient shutting himself up in it.
5. A bell to communicate with the outer ward should be provided. I should suggest a bell push over each bed.
6. The fireplace should be guarded by an effective fire guard closing in the whole fireplace such as is employed in asylums.'

By 1907 Dr Ricketts seems to have become obsessed by the incompetence of 'the race of stewards' and wrote tediously long letters on the shortcomings of the new one at Joyce Green. 'Perhaps the most remarkable of the (new) steward's defects is his repeated failure to execute the written instructions issued to him from these meetings of the Sub-Committee.' Two months later, in May 1908, the steward was duly dismissed, and Dr Ricketts wrote a carefully worded testimonial for him from which it is clear that the steward had been first a Steward's Clerk and then Assistant Steward, in both of which posts he had performed his duties entirely to the satisfaction of the Managers. Sadly, by being appointed Steward he had risen to his own level of incompetence and paid the price.

For the next 18 months Dr Ricketts acted as Steward, with no one looking over his shoulder to see how efficiently he performed his duties. To be fair, as the hospital was empty, he probably managed without any major trouble. However, everything did not go well and we find him writing letters of apology about a consignment of rotten pears and the amount of brussel sprouts (Suttons Exhibition) that they supplied to the children's infirmary. Then an order for 200 bags of potatoes was next to a letter about a sailor who got smallpox in Algiers, an example of his dual rôle.

It is to be hoped that the new steward, a Mr Furness, who took over in December 1909, was unaware of the tribulations of his predecessor. Mr Furness, who had been a non-commissioned officer in the Army, was put on probation for six months and in May 1910 Dr Ricketts reported 'I consider that Mr Furness should be confirmed in his appointment. He has fair ability and is probably as good an officer as the managers are likely to get to fill the position. I have no complaints to make as to his contract. He has not much initiative and further experience has shown that his attainments and technical knowledge are not of a high order, yet he is industrious and seems anxious to learn and I think he will make a steward of quite average capacity.'

Wisely perhaps Dr Ricketts continued to manage the farm with the bailiff and his successor Dr Cameron happily carried on doing the same. What Ricketts had started as a stop gap measure became Cameron's major preoccupation as judged by the size of his farm reports to the MAB.

In the summer of 1910 Dr Ricketts was ill for two months with what they called bronchial catarrh and in August 1911 he disappeared for one year, but at no point do the records indicate when it was established that he had pulmonary tuberculosis. The photographic record indicates that he took his ½ plate and stereo cameras with him and visited the Isle of Man, Ailsa Craig, Niagara Falls and Rhodesia, but whether this world tour had a beneficial effect on his health is not known. One person who may have found it hard to regret his absence was the new steward, Mr Furness, who could stamp his authority on the job without the feeling of somebody (and what a somebody) breathing down his neck.

After his return from the world tour the predominant theme of his letters concerned the future of the River Hospitals and the possible refurbishment of Long Reach, once it had been decided to restore it as the front line smallpox hospital and release Joyce Green as an overflow fever hospital.

His swan song after 21 years as Medical Superintendent came in 1913 when he put in a plea that Joyce Green should either be kept open or kept closed; what he could not abide being those sudden openings and closings. That sounds like the plea of a tired man. He continued 'I suppose I have had more experience of opening hospitals in a hurry than any man in the kingdom. The practice has its drawbacks, though monotony is not one of them. At all events I thought I knew the best and worst of it. I was mistaken. It is never easy under such conditions to obtain and organise a staff fast enough to keep pace with the requirements. That is one of the allurements of the pursuit. Now for the first time I found that staff — female staff — was not in fact scarce to get, but was not to be got. There was a shortage alike of nurses and domestics. The nursing staff has to be supplemented by a little army of institution nurses, hired at great expense, and the domestic staff until recently by a number of charwomen.' He writes in the style of one who knows he is leaving and is enjoying his Parthian shot or soldier's farewell. His successor, Dr A. F. Cameron, who had been acting MS during Ricketts' sick leave, was probably Dr Ricketts' personal choice. Outside medicine Dr Cameron had two outstanding qualities: he could enjoy a round of golf with Dr Ricketts on the hospital golf course and he was clearly a farmer *manqué*. Thus he was able to continue as farm manager, the role which Ricketts had taken on in 1907 when the steward proved incompetent.

Perhaps the best epitaph on Dr Ricketts is the one written 52 years after his death by Louis Jacobs of the American Public Health Service: 'T. F. Ricketts probably had the richest experience with the disease [smallpox] and used it to the best advantage of anyone in the world's history.'

Oct 30th 1

Dear Thomson

I should be glad if you could make it convenient to arrange your discharges as follows:—

Mon
Wed } women
Fri

Tues
Thurs } men
Sat

in order to avoid discharging patients of the two sexes on the same day

Yours faithfully
J. F. Ricketts

P.S.
Jas Leary & Saml Wiltshire, transferred today, Leeds asylum.

P.S. For next week (ending Nov 9th) my discharge days are as follows

Monday } women   Wednesday } men
Thurs   Sat

I shall probably have to send over some patients marked for discharge next week, as above, as we are very pressed for beds. J.R.

ABOVE: Letter from Dr Ricketts to Dr Thomson at Gore Farm Hospital in October 1901, about discharge plans during the smallpox epidemic. Segregation of the sexes! BELOW: Doctor Ricketts and his family at Southfield House, Joyce Green, where they lived 1898-1914. The house was built in 1879.

82

ABOVE: Beagles at Southfield House, Joyce Green buildings in the background. Dr Ricketts has his right hand in his pocket, facing the camera. There was no local pack and it is not known whence they came.
BELOW: This is possibly Dr Rickett's farewell Christmas Ball in 1914. Matron Wacher, with a large buttonhole, stands behind Dr Ricketts (seated centre of 2nd row). The Chaplain (1913-1934) was Rev F. de P. Castells AKC (back row). Many, blinded by the camera lights, have shut their eyes, including Dr Ricketts.

ABOVE: Dr Ricketts hands over to his successor, Dr A. F. Cameron, with a swing, but the unknown nurses are hardly dressed for the part. BELOW: Around 1915. the new MS, Dr Cameron, poses in a Joyce Green ward with polished parquet floor, and floral and female beauty. Seventy and more years on, the floors, though less shiny, are a tribute to the men who laid them.

THE FIGHT AGAINST SMALLPOX

'The Doctor paid off an old pox, By borrowing a new one from an ox.'

Byron, *Don Juan*, Canto 1.

'Where are you going to, my pretty maid?
I'm going a-milking sir, she said,
Sir she said, sir she said,
I'm going a-milking sir she said.

What is your fortune my pretty maid?
My face is my fortune sir she said,
Sir she said, sir she said,
My face is my fortune sir she said.'

The Milk Maid, Trad.

Isolation, disinfection and vaccination were the three main weapons in the fight against smallpox. Isolation was the prime function of the ships, followed by vaccination or revaccination of contacts and staff. Away from the ships, disinfection and vaccination in London were in disarray, even though the latter had been compulsory for over 10 years. In 1892 Dr Birdwood, the ships' first Medical Superintendent, reported that it was a matter of great regret that London had no central authority charged with the duties of tracing an outbreak of smallpox, and taking concerted action towards stamping it out, by methods of disinfection and vaccination or revaccination.

These measures still remained in the hands, partly of the 41 local sanitary authorities, partly of the Boards of Guardians, partly of the Local Government Board (LGB), and partly of the London County Council (LCC). The sequence of events likely to occur after the managers had isolated the patients in hospital was to give notice to the local sanitary authority, who instituted such measures of disinfection as may be thought necessary. 'The Boards of Guardians may then set in motion a vaccination officer and a public vaccinator, and lastly if they think proper to do so, either the LGB or the LCC or both, may make an inquiry as to the origins of the infection after a lapse of time.'

The use of the word 'may' seems to indicate that on occasions nothing was done. Amazingly Dr Birdwood was able to cite instances when the disinfectors, being unvaccinated, were themselves admitted to the ships, suffering from smallpox. He felt that, if the disinfection of the dwellings and effects of patients was entrusted to the MAB, it was likely that as marked an improvement would result as when they took over the metropolitan ambulance service in 1883. That a disinfector in 1892 should go about his duty unvaccinated is surprise enough, but an even greater surprise is that a few years later, officials of the MAB were coming on duty down to the ships unprotected by vaccination; and in the 1901 epidemic there were admitted to the hospital ships no fewer than 21 persons employed on disinfecting work, one of whom died, most of them being servants of Borough Councils. Not one of these persons had been revaccinated since infancy. Today this might be considered criminal negligence, but it reflects the apparent casual or even hostile attitude of the London populace and local government officials to vaccination. Hostility to vaccination had been rising in the country since the introduction of compulsion and especially since the Act of 1871, which made negligent parents liable for non-compliance; in default of fines and costs they could even be gaoled.

Much of the opposition arose from the high rate of illness and even death following vaccination. This opposition bore fruit in the form of the Royal Commission on Vaccination 1890, a copy of which was sent to the Ships, but Dr Birdwood is not listed among the witnesses; from his viewpoint there was nothing to argue about, for vaccination was a success, even if there was a certain morbidity. But the evidence of two objectors given to the Royal Commission may be taken as a fair sample of the layman's differing viewpoint.

Rev William Fox said that his daughter was refused a teaching appointment because she could not produce a vaccination certificate. He had joined the anti-vaccination lobby because his brother's son had died of the effects of vaccination, and he had hearsay evidence that children in his congregation had been crippled, and one died, by being vaccinated from the lymph of a child with smallpox. (That of course was not evidence against Jennerian vaccination, which used lymph from a cow with cowpox.) Another type of objector was John Henry Matthews, machinist, who had been harassed by the Magistrates about the vaccination of his children, despite medical certificates stating that they should not be vaccinated because of eczema. He was against the rigid enforcement of compulsory vaccination rather than in total opposition. In reality, it does seem, from looking at the smallpox patients' notes, that it was not too difficult to avoid vaccination in childhood, enforcement being poor, especially in the crowded slums of London. William Tebb, President of the London Society for the Abolition of Compulsory Vaccination, was the chief spokesman for the abolitionists and he produced witnesses and evidence from all over the globe in support of his case. Legislation in 1898 allowing conscientious objection to vaccination was the reward for his endeavours.

At Long Reach, vaccinating contractors' men was a major problem, as Dr Ricketts explained in his report for 1893. 'Workmen have as is natural a great objection to be vaccinated because if the operation is successful it is apt to prevent them from working. As a result they resort to all sorts of devices to evade vaccination. They make false statements as to the date they were last vaccinated, they assert that they have had smallpox, they exchange vaccination certificates, and assume the names of comrades who are known to be protected. Of course one discounts all their statements and takes all possible precautions against their evading the regulations. Very few in fact did succeed in evading them and it is remarkable that out of the five cases quoted above no less than four escaped vaccination by one means or another.'

George Field was a Dartford bricklayer who helped build Joyce Green Hospital and many years on he told a young acquaintance that, after vaccination, he sucked the fluid off his skin so as not to be incapacitated for work and lose pay. Men were desperate for work in those days, he explained. In 1897 Dr Ricketts had played a game of hide-and-seek with the timekeeper to the contractors who were building the tramway to Joyce Green. The timekeeper, who was not there every day, kept disappearing through a broken fence whenever there was a chance to vaccinate him. In 1902 the Board adopted the realistic policy of paying wages to any workmen while incapacitated by vaccination, and a statistically-minded vaccination officer was able to report that the average cost of vaccinating 587 workmen at Gore Farm Hospital was £1 15s $^{542}/_{587}$d. In 1905 the MAB still included in the contract for additional work at Joyce Green Hospital a condition that 'all workmen and those employed on or in any way connected with the works shall be revaccinated', and in May 1905 the sum of £88 8s 5d was allowed to certain of the temporary workmen at Joyce Green who were partly incapacitated by the effects.

In 1901 the Statistical Committee of the MAB summarised the evidence of the protective effect of vaccination on their employees, figures which were probably provided by Dr Ricketts. 'Of 2,198 persons employed at the smallpox hospitals between 1884 and 1900 inclusive, in which period 17,900 smallpox cases were received into the hospitals, only 17 persons contracted smallpox of whom 13 were not revaccinated until after they had joined the ship. Four were workmen who escaped medical observation. Not one of the staff of the hospital ships has ever died of smallpox and not one has even suffered from the disease for the past eight years.' But the anti-vaccinationists, who were strong at Purfleet on the Essex shore, were not impressed and as a result Purfleet suffered badly in the 1902 epidemic.

Dr Ricketts was understandably annoyed that a member of the MAB London staff should resist vaccination as did Mr Jarratt from the Accounts Department in 1901. 'I considered him insufficiently protected against smallpox but he objected to being revaccinated. But as I had no patients under treatment at that time I did not press the matter. Mr Jarratt again visited the hospital yesterday without notice and in my absence, and informed Dr Thompson who was acting for me that he still maintained his objections. I should not wish in the case of an officer in the chief office, to adopt the course I follow in the cases of other persons employed by the Managers and refuse him under such circumstances admission to the hospital. I should suggest therefore that before visiting this hospital again Mr Jarratt should take steps to be revaccinated and to furnish me with evidence of the success of the operation. I may take this opportunity of pointing out that other of your officers have recently been visiting this hospital while insufficiently protected against smallpox.' He names two people, one of whom had never been vaccinated in his life. A year later it was surprising to find that Mr Jarratt was back, still unrevaccinated. Dr Ricketts must have been angry when he wrote 'I assume that before his next visit he will take steps to comply with the Managers' regulations and I shall be obliged if you would direct him to send me before his next visit evidence of his successful revaccination.'

In 1896 there was an outbreak of smallpox in Gloucester, and he responded to an appeal for help. 'Dear Madam, I am willing to lend you the services of three nurses, but it must be on the clear understanding that they may be recalled at any time at a week's notice. The nurses are prepared to come for wages at the rate of £30 per year with outdoor uniform. They will also expect their railway fare and may wish to know whether washing is allowed. I presume it is. I may point out that these volunteers are giving up a salary of £40 per year to come to you. You should therefore not expect, and I certainly should not ask them to come to you for a smaller salary than that mentioned in your letter. Indeed I have taken the liberty of pointing out to them that there does not appear to be any particular call on their generosity since a municipal authority which courts an epidemic and in the consequent emergency offers a salary of £30 for competent smallpox nurses, is hardly to be pitied if it finds such nurses difficult to obtain.'

It must have been doubly hurtful that the native county of Jenner and Ricketts could have been so swayed by anti-vaccinationists that they had got into these difficulties, but at that time the Cheltenham Anti-Compulsory Vaccination League, a few miles down the road, was at the peak of its activities.

Despite the campaign in support of vaccination and revaccination the MAB's attitude towards visiting smallpox patients was casual in the extreme. Their handbook for 1906/7 says that 'if it be a smallpox hospital visitors are advised not to go into the wards without having been properly revaccinated and if they reside where the case visited occurred, are earnestly requested to urge the remainder of the occupiers of such a house to call at once upon the Public Vaccinator for the purpose of being vaccinated'. Visits to dangerously ill patients were limited to a quarter of an hour and only two visitors per patient were allowed. As an extra precaution, visitors were required to wear a wrapper provided by the Board, to cover their dresses and heads when in the ward, and to wash their hands and faces with carbolic soap and water before leaving the hospital, or to use such other mode of disinfection as might be directed by the Medical Superintendent.

Even after the 1898 Act allowing conscientious objection, the National Anti-vaccination League was still active. In 1904, after the epidemic was over, Dr Ricketts applied for a vivisection licence, his aim being to carry out experimental work in connection with the causation of smallpox. As Dr Ricketts may have expected, he experienced opposition on the MAB from a Mr Beurle, who had been one of the leading anti-vaccinationists and now reappeared as an anti-vivisectionist. In opposing the vivisection licence he urged the Board to pause before allowing a great moral wrong to be committed in its name. However, his move to block Dr Ricketts' experiments was defeated by 34 votes and the *The Lancet* (1904), which had obviously been keeping a watchful eye on events, was pleased that the Board wisely refused to take the hysterical view that wanton cruelty was being committed by certain Medical Officers.

However, Dr Ricketts' plans came to nothing, for there were insufficient patients with smallpox from whom to obtain the material for experimental inoculations of animals. As far as that project was concerned, Dr Ricketts and the River Hospitals had done their work too well and, though he did not know it, there would never be a massive outbreak of major smallpox again in the country. The medical journals continued to urge the need for revaccination and in 1905 the *British Medical Journal* went so far as to try to make revaccination an election issue; they wrote 'If every medical man would only take the opportunity of enlisting in favour of obligatory revaccination the sympathies of the candidate he supports, the new Parliament would undoubtedly be much more favourably disposed to proper legislation on this subject than the present Government have shown themselves to be'. But it was to be national insurance, not revaccination, which occupied the minds of the new Government and the population at large.

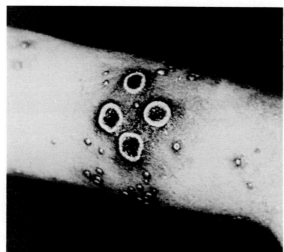

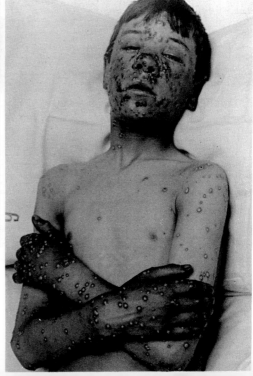

88

METROPOLITAN ASYLUMS BOARD.

HOSPITAL SHIPS.

Matron's Record of Service and Conduct of the undermentioned Officer or Servant.

Name in full	*Kate Godding*
•Age...	24 *Vaccinated 6ᵗ Aug 1901*
Position held	*Laundrymaid Promoted Ironer 1ˢᵗ Oct 190*
Date of Appointment	*14 Aug 1901*
Date of Leaving	*25 May 1902*
Cause of Leaving	*Resignation*

REMARKS.

To include a record of behaviour, with a statement whether ever reported to the Sub-Committee for any offence or misconduct, and a record of result of Sub-Committee's investigation.

General servant Mⁿ Garrett Fair View Bound Green Rd Bow Park Wood green 1 yr 6 mth.

General servant Mⁿ Saunders 11. Whitehall Parade, Highgate N.

S E Hospital Laundrymaid July 99 Aug 1900

Housemaid Malvern Hotel South Kensington 6 month

Laundress North London Truant School High St Walthamstow Essex. 4 month.

OPPOSITE LEFT: Successful vaccination, using four applications. Later one application was considered adequate; it gave as much immunity as the multiple approach and was less toxic. RIGHT: The way it attacked the face made smallpox more feared than other equally fatal conditions, like diphtheria. ABOVE: Record sheet of Kate Godding, typical of the many who, protected by vaccination, worked safely on the ships during the 1901/02 epidemic.

EATS AND DRINKS

1. Your pocket's lined with silver,
   Your barrel's full of beer
   Your pantry full of pork-pies
   I wish I had some here.

2. Go down into your cellar
   And see what you can find,
   The barrel is not empty,
   I hope you will prove kind.

   Souling rhymes recorded by
   Charlotte S. Burne.

It is perhaps surprising that the small details of life are often harder for the historian to discover than are the broad sweep of events. It is not known, for instance, if the author's 19th century ancestor, Sophia Burne, drank the beer she regularly brewed, faithfully recording the event in her diaries, along with the cheeses made and pigs killed. Or was it just for below stairs and the outside workers? To them beer was the normal long drink but, by the time the ships had anchored at Long Reach, the temperance movement was well established and doctors were no longer prescribing alcohol as freely as they had done in the first half of the 19th century.

This change of attitude is reflected in the menu of the Gore Farm Smallpox camp of 1883. Beer is given as an alternative to lemonade or milk and then only after a wholesome cup of tea or cocoa for starters. However, it needed a scandal in the MAB's Eastern Hospital in 1895 to produce a tightening up in the regulations about prescribing beer or wine. In this scandal a large amout of Beaune wine was said to have been consumed, notably by children. The inquiry learnt that, on 4 July, the diet sheet of the day contained entries amounting to 34 small bottles of Beaune and these were carried forward into the steward's account as 34 large bottles: 'Had it been consumed by the patients of this ward, who were mostly children, they would have been hopelessly intoxicated'. Even 34 small bottles of Beaune wine in one ward in one day is incredible to our ears. The strength of the temperance movement may indicate why Dr Ricketts was fierce with the staff, who brought in alcoholic drinks and consumed them in their bunk or cabin, so it is no surprise to find Nurse White resigning for having such a bottle in her possession.

It is a surprise to find that hospital staff still had a beer ration in 1897. At the Board's request, Dr Ricketts carried out a survey on the ships, and found that 20 out of 33 male staff received money in lieu of beer but only four out of 56 of the female staff still preferred the beer. One snag that arose from giving up beer was that they also had to give up a ration of aerated water. Dr Ricketts noted that a good many persons who took money formerly took aerated water; so perhaps the amount of beer drunk was not as high as the figures first suggest. Six weeks later, at the end of March 1897, there were 229 on the staff, and 177 of

OPPOSITE ABOVE: The galley of *Endymion*. Only two bulbs can be seen, so the new-fangled electric light cannot have been good. There is meat on the chopping block in the foreground, and at the far end, what may be melon slices. BELOW: G. Vinten, 4 High Street, Dartford, sold fish, poultry and ice to the Hospital Ships. By 1908 the shop was owned by Lipton. The site was redeveloped in 1989.

91

them received money in lieu of beer. No one knows when a beer ration ceased to be part of the emolument of MAB employees. It was still in existence in 1907 but for some reason ward and laundry maids and sewing room staff were excluded. Perhaps many were non-resident and it was thought they would just take it home to their menfolk.

On the hospital ships, the cooking was done on the galley of the *Endymion*, the middle one of the three ships, used solely for administration and services. In the photo of the galley it is not easy to identify the food, apart from the milk churns and meat on the chopping block. In May 1884 J. & E. Hall of Dartford supplied six new cooking boilers for the *Endymion* at a cost of £64, probably for making soup, or the beef tea favoured by Dr Ricketts.

Written records are informative, patients' notes record diets and extras, minutes tell us contractors' names and the Medical Superintendent reports on the problems — there were no lack of these. Because of local fear of smallpox it was often necessary to purchase food in London and bring it down on the ambulance steamers, always provided these were running. There was, in reality, little risk to local traders provided they were fully vaccinated, or better still revaccinated, for an adult who was vaccinated in childhood had little or no immunity left. Fish, eggs and milk were a continuing problem, but conditions improved once ice became commercially available after about 1890. It was shipped from various northern lands, wrapped in insulating material such as straw, and as a result milk could be kept cool and for the first time fresh fish appeared on the menu. By 1895 ice was being prescribed for patients, one little girl having it added to her supplementary milk, and an ice compress to her neck. That was in March, but the story might have been different in high summer because of problems of storage.

The patients had a range of standard diets including Sick 1 or 2, Middle and Full. We do not know their content but supplements such as milk, eggs, fish, B and B pudding (bread and butter?) were sometimes prescribed, and brandy was the universal stimulant, one dying two-year-old getting half a dram every half hour up to three ounces (8 fluid drachms = 1 fluid ounce. Apothecaries' weight). From about 1894 beef tea was the backbone of the diet, and Dr Ricketts was keen that it should be properly prepared, as the following memo shows: 'According to the dietary scale in force at the hospital until recently, soup was allowed for sick patients and beef tea was not specified. It was made from shin of beef in an ordinary soup kettle. Very good beef tea or soup could be prepared in this way but it depended on the care or the skill of the person making it. Recently the cook and most of the old hands in the kitchen have left and I have had to complain more than once about the preparation of the beef tea and other articles of diet. A short time back I directed that beef tea, prepared according to the recognised formula, should be substituted in the dietary scale for soup and I pointed out to the steward that lean meat should be used instead of shin of beef. He has, at my request, obtained a price of such meat from the present meat contractor, who will submit it to you. I have also asked him to obtain a price for a water jacket apparatus, such as should be used for making beef tea'. The meat contractor may have been Reuben Message of Dartford, who was also a local Councillor but unfortunately he employed an unvaccinated delivery man to take the meat down to Long Reach.

The first camp for smallpox patients at Gore Farm lasted from April 1884 to September 1885 and, after it was closed, Dr Waylen, the Medical Superintendent, wrote a very full report to the Darenth Camps Committee of the MAB. Cooking was by gas from the Darenth Asylum, which had its own gasworks, supplemented by an open fire roaster capable of roasting 400 lbs of meat at one time. By this roaster the entire supply for each camp was roasted on alternate days. He reports that the meals were ample, varied and unlimited. Clearly the authorities made a great effort to provide a well-balanced, nutritious, digestible diet, with alcoholic stimulation for the seriously ill. One quarter's accounts for the hospital ships during the 1901 epidemic show purchases of meat, fruit and vegetables, potatoes, lemons, cheesemongery, grocery and eggs, ale, milk and cream, champagne and burgundy, but no fish, which was supplied to Gore Farm Convalescent Hospital. Fortunately the amount of wine and beers consumed does not suggest the existence of a fiddle as took place in the aforementioned Eastern Hospital in 1884.

A study of the accounts of the MAB at that time discloses how small were the payments for vegetables and fruit, none at all in the quarterly account for the hospital ships in the autumn of 1902, except only £10 worth of lemons bought of W. T. Jay; we may make a reasonable guess that they were to prevent scurvy. This absence of fresh vegetables is not to be wondered at, because the green stocked shelves in today's superstores are a by-product of modern refrigeration and air travel, and unknown for the first 60 years of this century. Pease potage hot, pease potage cold, pease potage in the pot, nine days old, was real to our ancestors.

Thirty years separated the ships from Dr Cameron's Joyce Green which, in the inter-war years, must have been nearly self-supporting for part of the year. He proudly reported to the MAB on the produce of its farm, its vegetable garden and its orchard. Milk, eggs, meat, apples and pears, rhubarb, strawberries and loganberries were available in their seasons for the enjoyment of patients and staff alike.

After the war the hospital farm continued with increasing difficulties into the 1960s, surviving a nationwide outbreak of foot and mouth disease and a disastrous local outbreak of swine fever. But no longer did its produce go to the hospital kitchens; capital investment for dilapidated buildings was not forthcoming and the supply of suitable patients from Darenth Park dried up, those with sufficient intelligence being put back into the community. Breaking point was reached when the farm manager, Mr Larkins, discovered that one such man was battering some of the piglets and hiding their bodies in a compost heap.

But, echoing Dr Cameron, it would be nice if upwards of 76 lbs of hospital grown strawberries were still available each year for the enjoyment of the staff. The land is still there, but the will has gone.

By c1950 a wide range of diets was on offer now that Joyce Green was a
general hospital. Staff uniform had changed too.

94

ASHORE AND AT WAR

'So twice five miles of fertile ground,
With walls and tower were girded round
And there were gardens bright with sinuous rills
Where blossomed many an incense bearing tree.'
Kubla Khan by S. T. Coleridge.

Once the decision had been made to close the ships and move onto land, things proceeded at breakneck speed, stimulated by the massive outbreak of smallpox in 1901. The temporary Long Reach Hospital with 300 beds opened in 1902, a larger temporary hospital of 800 beds was built in two years on the site of a nearby orchard from which it took its name and, at the end of 1903, the permanent Joyce Green Smallpox Hospital was opened. So by 1904 there were three hospitals with a total of nearly 2,000 beds on 315 acres of land on or adjacent to the Dartford marshes, including the whole of Marsh Street Farm. Thus farm management became a major preoccupation of the MS and Steward. Add to these the 1,800 beds of the Gore Farm Convalescent Hospital, and the MAB in 1904 had nearly 4,000 beds for smallpox, but only a handful of patients.

The three hospitals grouped near the Thames – The Orchard, Long Reach and Joyce Green — were collectively known as the River Hospitals and administered by a Medical Superintendent, Steward and Matron. Gore Farm had its own MS and supporting staff. The River Hospitals kept their collective name for over 60 years, the title fading from common usage, especially after the destruction of the Orchard by fire bombs in 1940, until in 1973 only Joyce Green was left. From the first the farming was taken seriously, but the estate within the perimeter fence of Joyce Green was somewhat neglected until Dr Cameron took matters in hand after the 1914/18 War.

Hay was produced in excess of the needs of the farm and hospital and was a useful source of income. In 1899 Messrs E. Underwood & Son paid £1,050 for 18 stacks, which were partly on upland around Joyce Green and partly on marsh near Long Reach Hospital, the whole to be removed before 30 June 1900. An attempt by the Steward to remove some of the hay by water from the hospital's pier head was thwarted by Dr Ricketts, who was obviously glad of an opportunity to assert his authority.

'Dear Mr. Moule, I have received from Norfolk House a copy of your letter re removal of hay by Messrs Underwood. I hope you do not think I am pulling your leg about this. In giving

OPPOSITE ABOVE: Joyce Green kitchen, c1920. Clock by Maple & Co London. BELOW: Joyce Green stores, c1920. Split peas, haricot beans and rice must have been the staple diet. Box for Long Reach Hospital on left.

them permission to use the pier head I supposed you had some authority for doing so, as appears from your letter to be the case; but as I did not remember the Committee agreeing to it, I thought the arrangement was probably sanctioned by the Chief Office. I could not afford to have a precedent of this kind created without comment. Remember that we shall soon have the contractors of the new hospital and they will be wanting to use the pier head for the same purpose. The risk is a very real one and is not to be got over merely by enforcing the regulation as to vaccination. We cannot treat these men like staff and insist on their being successfully vaccinated before they begin work. To protect myself therefore I prefer it to be clearly understood that if permission to use these premises is given to persons whose entry within the gates is not necessary to the hospital I do not concur in sanctioning the arrangement. You will therefore understand I hope that this is not in anyway a personal matter between us and I am making no complaint about you.'

To us Dr Ricketts may seem to be making rather heavy weather over a one-off situation, but it does emphasise the difficulty of trying to run a farm and a smallpox hospital as a composite whole. Two years later the hay storm blew up again, but this time it was a new gate on the land side that caused the problem.

The third of the River Hospitals, the 800-bed Orchard, was little more than a white elephant, and Dr Ricketts had expressly stated that he had always opposed its building. However, there it was, and in its first 12 years of life it was used but once and then as a fever overflow hospital. It was never used for smallpox, which was its original purpose, but its moment of glory came in 1915 when, for four years, it became No 3 Australian Auxiliary Hospital, which moved there at the end of the ill-fated Gallipoli campaign. The Hospital returned home in 1919 with, surprise, surprise, a bride or two from Dartford, leaving behind a souvenir magazine laced with a mixture of humour, sadness at the loss of colleagues, and a rhyming dialogue comparing Aussie girls back home with the Pommy version. 'I've got a bonza little girl, I met her up in town. I'm balmy on her. She's a pearl, should ought to wear a crown.' A rather blurred photo taken in 1917 shows a group of convalescent Aussies beside a crashed plane from nearby Joyce Green Airfield, and another of 'the hole in the wall' where those who had stayed out late were climbing in, hoping not to be caught. Occasional inquiries from descendants of these Dartford Australian marriages are received at Joyce Green but the records went with the hospital, for it was run as an autonomous organisation. Dr Cameron's reports to the MAB did not refer to it.

In the early 1920s the Orchard did a stint as a fever hospital and the cameraman paid the hospital a visit. He left us an intimate glimpse of a ward together with the obligatory potted plants, testimony to the urge for floral beauty which followed the four dark years of war. The Orchard Hospital sprang to life again after Dunkirk, then disappearing like a dying star into a black hole, for much of it was destroyed by fire bombs shortly after the refugees had left. Thereafter, the few remaining buildings were converted to farm use, the discharge ward became a dutch barn, the tramshed a cow shed, and the boiler house used for steaming pig swill.

Joyce Green's career was equally unexpected; it carried on as a fever hospital for much of the Great War until it too sprang into action in July 1918 with the arrival, at a week's notice, of 1,000 war refugees. The rapid preparation to receive refugees was made possible by the presence of German prisoners-of-war at the Southern Hospital, now called Dartford War Hospital, who were able to fill the great gap in manpower in this country. Being smallpox contacts, the refugees were all revaccinated but, as only two were found to have the disease, it must have seemed the least of their worries. Indeed, Dr Cameron, the MS since 1915, found that about 90 others were ill in some way, one dying of 'flu, a foretaste of the pandemic which killed, by repute, more than died in four years on the battlefield. The refugees disappeared from our records as quickly as they appeared, including 16 sick and wounded Serbian soldiers.

The return of peace brought a long list of repairs and alterations, an award to Dr Cameron from the King of Italy for unspecified services, and also a major outbreak of scarlet fever, which filled Joyce Green, overflowed into the Orchard and laid low as many as 40 staff in one month.

By 1923 Joyce Green was empty and Dr Cameron was able to turn his attention to the decaying Long Reach Hospital. This, having avoided demolition after 1903, was now the official smallpox hospital and in urgent need of repair. Plans to rebuild it had been made before the war but came to nothing so, when these plans were revived in 1925, they were redrawn to take account of current thinking, notably isolation units and electric light. Unfortunately rebuilding coincided in 1928 with a major outbreak of variola minor (alastrim), the mild form of smallpox, so Joyce Green, for the first and only time in its life, was filled with the disease for which it was built.

Dr Cameron's chief function was in the diagnosis of smallpox and for this purpose he kept a notebook which he took with him when he visited suspected cases in various parts of London. However, smallpox had virtually disappeared from this country during the war and so, from taking up his post as Medical Superintendent in 1915, he was able to concentrate on the state of the grounds at Joyce Green. He started at once in November 1915, when he complained that great difficulty was being experienced in filling the position of Night Superintendent of Nurses. 'The weather conditions especially in winter on this exposed site are so trying that none of the sisters is willing to undertake the work and when one is induced to do so by an appeal to her sense of duty her tenure of the post is likely to be soon interrupted by her resignation.'

After the War he was able to return to the bleak windswept theme and his plea did not go unanswered, for Joyce Green became recognised as a plant propagation centre for the other Institutions of the MAB and, with the assistance of his gardener, Henry W. Hopkins, in 15 dynamic years he produced the marvellous grounds we know today. Glimpses of progress may be obtained from his reports to the MAB, 4 June 1919: 'The shrubs and trees recently planted are mostly thriving although the poplars were of a rather disappointing quality. I think that it would be expedient to retain the services of temporary labourer, Joyce, for orchard work because I am afraid that we shall find the same difficulty as in former years in obtaining the properly qualified workmen for cutting out and grafting of which there is much to be done before this fruit season is over. Joyce is over age for the permanent staff.' Despite the association of names there is no evidence that he was in any way connected with the original Joyce.

Later in 1919 he reports that '494 trees, poplars, sycamores and laburnums, a few conifers and thorns have been planted as well as over 600 flowering and evergreen shrubs and nearly 500 yards of a hedge consisting of golden privet, common privet and euonymus.' In 1922, work in the grounds made steady progress and a considerable number of better class new plants were introduced; a first indication of his zeal in building up a collection of hardy exotics. In 1923 he requested that the Board consider giving gardener Hopkins a reward for all his hard work and the Board responded to the tune of £20. He reported that over 3,000 plants had been sent to other institutions with a value of approximately £110.

It is clear that he was always anxious to convince his masters that his garden project was cost-effective. One way of doing this was to produce vegetables, for the land around Marsh Street farm was, and still is, good. In 1925 he was particularly proud of the 76 lbs of strawberries which enabled the staff to have an ample supply in season, there was an adequate quantity of loganberries (but he does not give a figure) and plenty of rhubarb. In 1922 25 calves were born, 65 pigs were slaughtered, 345 chickens reared and 22,946 eggs produced; but there were problems — tuberculosis amongst the cows, in 1925 the turkey rearing failed and swine fever broke out in 1928. The orchard was not doing well and, though he tried to introduce new types of apples and pears, it was grubbed up at some stage and is now the cricket pitch.

Dr Cameron's last gardening note was the request to move a mulberry and a weeping elm to make room for the nurses' mess room. The mulberry may be one of the two blown down in the hurricane of 16 October 1987, a sad end. The portrait of Dr Cameron painted by one of his assistants (Dr Bill Coughlan) was that of a disciplinarian and an efficient administrator, best avoided when on the warpath. He was asthmatic, made worse when he was angry, but survived his 1936 retirement by 28 years, a tribute perhaps to the soothing effect of a wife (Matron Morris) and the South African air to which they retired. So far as is known Cameron left no published work, his memorial being the beautiful grounds of Joyce Green Hospital which have survived remarkably well for 50 years, the single biggest act of destruction being, not the hand of man, but the hurricane force winds of October 1987. He was also instrumental in erecting a memorial to his highly praised, green-fingered gardener, Henry Hopkins. Thus it is that the most distinctive memorial in Joyce Green is a garden seat economically made from the bricks of the old Long Reach Hospital laundry. The plaque on the back of the seat reads 'Henry Hopkins, gardener, 1913 to 1935 planted these grounds'. In his report to the MAB Cameron eulogised Hopkins: 'When he returned from War Service he succeeded in transforming the grounds of his hospital from a wilderness covered by rough grass, with a few trees, into a garden in which month by month the flowers and fruits of an enormous variety of flowering plants and shrubs make a remarkable display'. There is no doubt where Dr Cameron's heart lay.

With the outbreak of war, Joyce Green underwent a dramatic change of fortune and direction, from fevers and smallpox to a general hospital, from LCC to Emergency Medical Service (EMS), and from intermittent to continuous use; indeed it had been empty for much of the three preceding years. After a false alarm in 1938 with the Munich crisis, the hospital's career as an EMS hospital started in earnest in August 1939, and the reports of MS Dr Mitman to the LCC dried up till 1941, when he summarised the events of the previous 20 months. Beds had been increased from 986 to 1,500, some being for service sick and casualties. Ten special units were set up, including three X-ray departments, the one in 8A being for a now-discredited form of skin therapy. Nurses came down with their patients from London and D isolation was converted into lecture and demonstration rooms. Accommodation had to be found for six categories of staff, including an RAMC detachment commanded by a military registrar with the rank of Major. ARP and blackout arrangements were still unsatisfactory after 20 months of war, which had brought 64 high explosive bombs and 200 incendiaries. The Orchard Hospital was badly damaged and its career summarily ended, but no Joyce Green building received a direct hit, and the only fatality was a member of the bomb disposal squad on duty in the hospital.

Dr Mitman's next report was dated 24 September 1945, when there were 428 patients in the hospital; all were civilians except 23 from the Netherlands, who were housed in H block, given over to the Dutch military authorities for their own use. With so much plate glass, H block had been considered too dangerous to use at the beginning of the war but this no longer applied once the flying bomb danger had passed. He reported 'The cessation of War has been followed by a decline in the activities of the hospital with a corresponding fall in the numbers of EMS and military staff as well as of the LCC nursing staff. At present nurses are available from several London hospitals, but in future nurses from St. Mary Abbott's Hospital will not be lent here'.

Not a single ward or other building had escaped bomb damage entirely and many were repeatedly damaged. Blackout paint was still present in many places but gas and most blackout curtains had been removed with the help of patients and staff, as had sandbags; in only two wards had the bricked up windows been removed. The blast walls were still present. The total number of occasions on which the hospital was bombed was 31, but after the 1940 blitz little happened till the V1 and V2 campaign; then one flying bomb, one part of a flying bomb, which exploded over the hospital, and one V2 rocket fell. In addition eight flying bombs and one rocket fell within sufficient proximity to the hospital to cause damage by blast. VE and VJ day celebrations were held but the details are missing, except that patients were allowed to take tea with their relatives and much enjoyed the privilege. However, in his report of 24 June 1946, he was more explicit about the victory celebrations. There was a bonfire with fireworks and a dance for all grades of staff with free refreshments and ices. Nor were the patients forgotten:

Patients Menu

Breakfast ....Grapefruit
Fried bacon & Sausages
Dinner ....Roast Lamb, Baked potatoes,
Tinned peas
Fruit salad, ice cream
Minerals or beer
Cigarettes
Tea ....Iced cake (made in Kitchen)
Tinned cakes (Gift from New Zealand)
Supper ....Cold ham and salad.

Dr Mitman's reign as the all-powerful Medical Superintendent had less than two years to run for, in 1948, the NHS took over from the LCC and, at the time of his death in 1957, he was little more than one of the three fever physicians, the other two being Drs Marsden and Coughlan still in post from the LCC days; they quickly became front line soldiers when a case of smallpox or suspected smallpox was admitted to Long Reach. As smallpox experts for the Ministry of Health they acted as roving consultants and in the hospital they maintained the vaccination state for those members of staff who might be exposed to risk when smallpox cases were admitted to Long Reach. As smallpox became rare, reluctance to be revaccinated increased and, in the final swansong of smallpox in 1973, a rush of staff to be vaccinated was not for fear of acquiring smallpox but because the Spanish and other authorities were suddenly demanding a valid vaccination certificate from English holiday-makers.

In January 1962 Long Reach Hospital briefly hit the headlines when *Parish Match* in an article called ALERTE featured this 'Vieux Lazaret de Dortford', which had recently reopened for a smallpox patient from India. 'Atmosphere' for the article was created by a picture of a warning notice-board at Long Reach. In the background was Joyce Green boiler-house chimney, belching black smoke; this was misinterpreted as the incinerator. It is known the caption said that a man came to die and that they incinerated his clothes, his bedclothes, his mattress and all his belongings. The background to the article was a fear that this disease of the Middle Ages would once again be widely disseminated, but by 'les jets', which at that time were becoming the mass transport round the world so readily accepted nowadays.

A patients' library at Joyce Green was an unexpected benefit of war, stocked and staffed by the British Red Cross Society with the dynamic figure of Lady Astor in the background. By

1945 there were nearly 3,000 books which, until the discard stage, were not available for TB and skin patients. The one library expenditure throughout the war years was £4 from a local legacy (Dryden), for books for tuberculous patients. This wartime voluntary effort, which ended in 1946, also left a legacy of pictures in Red Cross frames, and some of these are still around 40 years later. The Red Cross Voluntary Service was replaced by a paid fulltime Librarian and, though development was slow, the service has continued to expand without break and is now impressively comprehensive.

Throughout most of the war years Matron Hyde was the nursing supremo. She retired in October 1944 and died in 1954 when Dr Mitman, then MS in little more than name, recorded that her most outstanding achievement was her contribution to the enormous task of converting Joyce Green Hospital from an empty fever hospital to a war emergency hospital of 1,500 beds. 'Her forthright manner disconcerted malefactors both high and low, but she was quite unperturbed by their reactions. The standards she demanded were high and it was refreshing to see her experienced eye light upon anything which failed to reach her standard and demand its correction no matter in whose department it occurred. Her love of children was matched by her love of animals.' In the obituary one can detect a faint nostalgia for the good old days when the Matron, the MS and the Steward reigned supreme. In 1957 Dr Mitman, who had already had a previous mild heart attack, died in post with his faithful dog Butch by his side, a rather sad and wistful figure, who had gradually become reconciled to his loss of power. His chief memorial is the text book *Clinical Practice in Infectious Diseases* of which he was a joint author the 4th edition being published in 1951 when he was at Joyce Green.

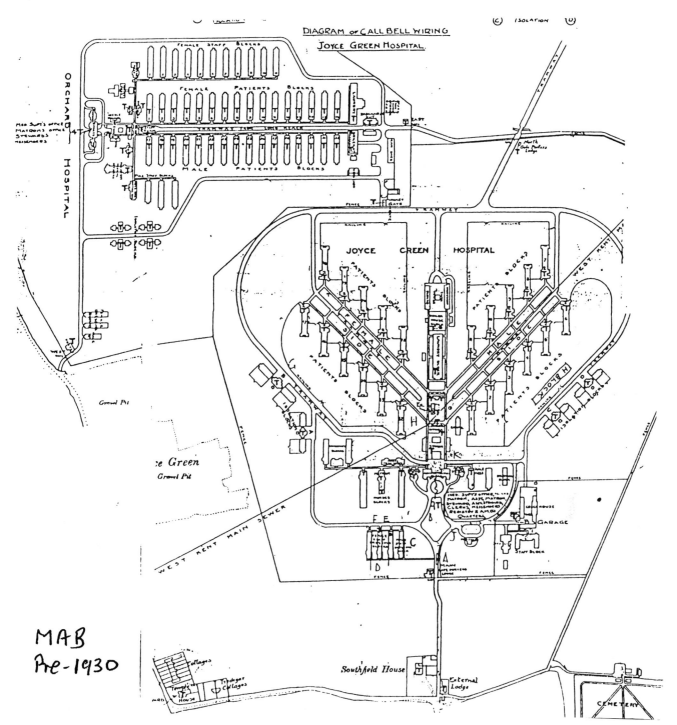

ABOVE: Plan of Joyce Green (98 acres) and Orchard (63 acres) Hospitals. OPPOSITE: Joyce Green Laboratory 1920, with a hand operated centrifuge clamped to the far end of the table.

Joyce Green Dispensary. The date on the bunny calendar is 1920. Miss Yates was dispenser in 1918-1929, and her sister was at the Southern.

ABOVE: Joyce Green's covered ways c1919 when Dr Cameron and gardener Hopkins started planting, and BELOW: the same 70 years on; proof that one plants trees for the next generation. Are we as far-seeing? (A)

ABOVE: View of South Gate Joyce Green, c1925. Coal trolleys INSET: await a delivery from Dartford. The cemetery is to the left along the road at the foot of Temple Hill, which is now a housing estate. BELOW: The sewing room is now the library. The parquet floor has survived 85 years of wear and tear well, but the places where the machines were screwed down are still visible.

ABOVE: Another relic from the tram days; the 3-bay wet-weather terminal in Chapel Street. (A) CENTRE: Orchard Hospital from offices, female lines on the left. Note roughly laid tramlines. (DL) BELOW: Orchard Hospital sanitary annexes of wards.

ABOVE: In 1917 Orchard Hospital was the 3rd Australian Auxiliary Hospital. (DL) CENTRE: The West Gate had a guard, but there was an 'ole in the fence for those out late. (DL) BELOW: Convalescent Australians inspect a crashed Vickers near the Hospital. It came from nearby Joyce Green airfield. (DL)

their track, and would periodically place a picquet on this said 'ole, whose duty it was to apprehend all intruders with a view to charging them with " A.W.L. and Breaking into Hospital." Whether these intruders were seriously dealt with need not be here mentioned now that we will soon be home, but the fact remains that they would be apprehended. In order to explain more clearly, and to give the readers of this magazine a better idea of this better 'ole, a series of snapshots have been supplied, which, of course, exaggerate the happenings considerably, but the " Better 'Ole " can be seen clearly and the unfortunate picquet on duty. The first depicts the picquet on duty, when the
" Late-coming Digger is sighted." He would have probably escaped had it not been for the reinforcements arriving, and thus
" Preventing an escape." After a desperate struggle for freedom the late comer
" Is Outed," and the unofficial work commences of
" Searching for souvenirs." (Let it here be clearly understood that this is only faked, and no truth whatever bears on this part of the story.) After emptying the contents of the pockets of the late comer.
" The spoils are equally divided," and the offender is considered a prisoner, and is
" Carried to the Guard Room," where he is detained for the night and charged as aforesaid " A.W.L. and attempting to break into Hospital." However, many a happy evening has been spent owing to the " Better 'Ole," and many a happy night will be spent in spite of the careful search and check of all wards, but, as one Digger has said: " As long as a man is respectable and sober, and causes no damage to property, what harm is there?" No harm at all. It is, we are given to understand, the intentions of the regular late comers to ask to have the track for the " Better 'Ole " repaired, as it is getting very disagreeable.   EDITOR.

* * *

" THE AUSTRALIAN GIRL'S LAMENT."

Once I had lovers in plenty,
  Before the boys left for Berlin;
I had ten before I was twenty—
  How happy the moments were then.
Their loss I could not discover,
  For love sweetened days' happy swing;
When each new week brought a new lover,
  The time it seemed always like spring.

But Cupid's sharp little pinion
  Could never keep up with the time.
So old age assumed its opinion
  When those four years of strife rang their
    chime.
Now, come back, while the time's ripening,
  To your girl, while the youths moments last,
Which closely around the heart twining
  Will live, when you return at last. NAGERO.

"AUSTRALIAN SOLDIER'S FAREWELL TO THE BEST GIRL IN ENGLAND."

The day I had to say good-bye,
  What grief it gave to me,
And scarcely did an hour pass by
  Unless I think of thee.

And of the pretty dainty hands,
  The movements full of grace,
And saw once more, as in a dream,
  Thy handsome shining face.

And then I think of those blest times
  Before we had to part,
When I could press thee close and feel
  The beating of thy heart.

And now that I have gone far from thee,
  And a brighter day will dawn
When I can send for thee out back
  To come and share with me my throne.
            NAGERO.

* * *

HISTORIC BATTLES.

Inquisitive Visitor: " Poor boy. What big battles were you in?"
Anzac: " I was in the battle of the Wasah and Fleurbaix and Longbay, Bullicourt and Earl's Court, Passchendale and Annandale. Dickiebush and Shepherds Bush."
Inquisitive Visitor: " Dear me! It's time all you originals were sent home."

ABOVE AND OVERLEAF: Pages from an Australian souvenir magazine, 1919.

THE TRANSPORT SERGEANT'S CHRISTMAS EVE, 1918.

ABOVE: Soon after the Australians left, the Orchard Hospital was full of fever patients who had come down the river from South Wharf, Bermondsey. The potted palm was a photographic 'must' in 1920.
BELOW: Post-war air view of Joyce Green and Orchard Hospitals shows extent of blitz damage to latter.

ABOVE: Long Reach Hospital post-1953 flood. Plinths of buildings removed on left. BELOW: Matron Couzins and Pat Hornsby-Smith MP launch out from North Gate for Long Reach Hospital on 1 February 1953.

LEFT: Dr M. Mitman, the River Hospital's fourth and last Medical Superintendent 1938-1957, and his dog Butch.

ABOVE RIGHT: Elsie Couzins was the last of five matrons who served the River Hospitals over 65 years, seen here at a farewell to Dr J. P. Marsden in 1965. Her successor had a number. BELOW: Dr J. P. Marsden's farewell, with Mrs Marsden. He was the last of the MAB smallpox experts who played a key role in ridding London of smallpox.

Darenth Asylum, where it all began, stands empty in 1989. The water (tower on left) came from wells under the Asylum, and enabled the MAB to establish their 1881 smallpox camp in a matter of two weeks. The Asylum also made their own gas which they piped to Gore Farm Hospital in 1884. (A)

APPENDIX 1

Darenth Camp	1881	Tents in grounds of Asylum
Hospital Ships	1884	*Atlas, Endymion* & *Castalia* at Long Reach
	1886	Lit by Electricity
	1902	Ships closed and sold for scrap (1904)
Long Reach Hospital	1902	Opened during epidemic. 324 beds
	1903	Patients to Joyce Green
	1907	Reinstated 'in a condition of instant readiness for smallpox'
	1928–31	Reconstruction. 252 beds. Electric light
	1931–34	Reopen, mild smallpox epidemic
	1953	Flooded; partially restored
	1962	Called 'un vieux lazaret' by *Paris Match*
	1973	Last smallpox patients
	1975	Bashed & burned. Hospital site used for new flood barrier
Orchard Hospital	1902	Opened but rarely used. 800 beds
	1915–19	Australians. Joyce Green Airfield adjacent
	1919–22	Fever cases, mostly scarlet
	1940	June, Dunkirk refugees. September, empty; destroyed by fire bombs. Conversion to farm, mainly pigs
Joyce Green Hospital	1903	Opened 28 Dec. 12/940 beds occupied
	1907	Used for fevers
	1918	1,000 refugees from Russia (SP contacts)
	1919–35	Intensive tree & shrub planting
	1926	Lit by electricity
	1928–31	Smallpox epidemic (variola minor). Death rate low
	1939–45	EMS Hospital
	1944–46	Dutch Military Hospital H Block
Gore Farm/Southern Hospital	1884	Tented smallpox camp. 1,000 beds
	1887	Hutted (lower) hospital. 850 beds. Extended 1902
	1890	Brick (upper) hospital, 964 beds
	1903	Redesignated, not for smallpox
	1911	Renamed Southern Hospital
	1915–19	Lower: Dartford War Hospital for Germans
	1918–19	Upper: US Base Hospital No 5
	1939–45	EMS hospital & Naval unit from Chatham
	1950–85	Lower: part demolished, part Mabledon Polish Hospital
	1959	Upper: demolished
Ambulance Steamers	1884	Service started with 4 paddle steamers *Maltese Cross, Red Cross, Albert Victor, Marguerite*
	1894	*Geneva Cross* in service. Electric light
	1895	Thames frozen for two weeks (February)
	1897	Pinnace *White Cross, Red Cross I* sold
	1902	*Red Cross II* from L & SW Rly. Busiest year
	1907	Least busy year (1 patient)
	1930	LCC takes over. Service closes
	1933	Steamers sold & pier demolished (1936)
	1940	South Wharf Rotherhithe blitzed

APPENDIX 2

The Ambulance Steamers
belonging to the Metropolitan Asylums Board

Note: the names of the ships will be in *italics*.

The Swallow, Steam Pinnace. Length, 42 feet; breadth, 8 feet 5 inches; depth, 5 feet; draught, 3 feet. March 1894 found to have defective timbers of hull. Passenger Certificate not renewed. Replaced in 1897 by *White Cross.*

Albert Victor, Paddle Steamer. Length, 132 feet 6 inches; breadth, 17 feet; depth, 7 feet 6 inches; draught, about 4 feet. Purchased for £3,150 of the London Steamboat Company in May 1884 and altered to render it suitable for ambulance purposes. Two Hospital cabins – one fore and the other aft – to accommodate 30 recumbent adult acute cases. In 1902 converted to carry 300 clean people. April 1931, transferred to LCC berth at Woolwich Ferry for sale. (Prince Albert Victor eldest son of the Prince of Wales, later Edward VII, died 1892).

Red Cross I, Paddle Steamer. Length, 105 feet; breadth, 16 feet 6 inches; depth, 7 feet 6 inches; draught, 4 feet 6 inches. First voyage February 1884. Designed by Mr Adam Miller, NA. Built by Edwards & Symes, Cubitt Town. Hull principally of iron with a strong keel. Silent discharge steam apparatus. Six water-tight compartments. Small room for crew forward of below deck infectious section. Capacity 16 acute or 50 sitting patients. Captain's saloon near stern end. Disposal: redundant when *White Cross* came into service and sold for undisclosed price in June 1898.

Red Cross II, Paddle Steamer. Length, 130 feet 9 inches; breadth, 18 feet; mean draught 4 feet 8 inches. Built at Southampton for the London & South Western Railway in 1900 and named 'Solent'. Purchased from Railway in 1902 for £7,750. Sixty-five lamp electric lighting, installed at a cost of £410. Speed 10½ knots. Certified to carry 300 ordinary passengers but after conversion capacity 68 recumbent patients. In non-epidemic times forward hospital (24 recumbent patients) used for staff, visitors etc. Left Southampton 21 January 1902 arriving South Wharf 23 January. Note: after completion by Messrs Mordey Carney at Southampton found to be unsuitable for planned use on Lymington–Southampton run, draught too great for Lyminge at low tide.

Maltese Cross, Paddle Steamer. Length 132 feet; breadth, 16 feet 6 inches; depth, 7 feet 6 inches; draught, 3 feet. Cost of construction and fitting up, £5,860. Brought into use October 1884. Two Hospital cabins – one fore and the other aft – of the same size, divided into two parts, each part accommodating 8 adult cases in a recumbent position.

Geneva Cross, Paddle Steamer. Length, 143 feet; breadth, 22 feet; draught, 5 feet. Cost of construction and fitting £10,980 8s 8d. Built by Messrs J. Stewart & Son to a design prepared by Chas Thompson for the MAB. Satisfactory trial runs under steam in June 1894 when the electric machinery was also tested. First voyage 13 July 1894. Accommodation: upper and lower hospital cabins at stern end, upper cabin 16 acute patients in two compartments. Lower cabin 36 patients in two compartments. Cabin in fore part for visitors.

White Cross, Screw Launch. Length, 65 feet; breadth, 12 feet 6 inches; mean draught, 2 feet 7 inches. Cost of construction and fitting up £2,049. Built 1896 by Edwin Clark at Brimscombe Port, Stroudwater Canal, Gloucestershire. Accommodation: fore part cabin for staff and visitors, after part cabin, four recumbent patients. Moved to Temple Pier, London via Bristol and Kennet & Avon Canal, 12–22 December 1896. One day's delay at Newbury due to fatal accident. Rough cast propeller fitted for journey. First voyage for MAB 15 March 1897. Reliable & economic to run. Disposal: 2 June 1929 to LCC for transport of water samples.

Marguerite, Paddle Steamer. Length overall 73 feet, breadth 16 feet. Built 1879 by Messrs Edwards & Symes. Acquired 1884. Cost £1,075 + £126 repairs. October 1886, needs new boiler. Test run at Long Reach measured mile, mean speed 8½ knots. Sold October 1889 to Messrs Brown & Co of Fenchurch Street for £200. Acquired for use by visitors to seriously ill patients and by Ships staff, but cannot have been a success.

Conservator, Paddle steamer. Acquired during peak period of 1902 smallpox epidemic. February, surveyed and tested. 13 March, handed over in West India dock. No cost given. 21 March, first journey to Long Reach from South Wharf in 1 hour 10 minutes wind & tide in her favour. Return journey 2 hours. Disposal November 1903.

Disposal of three remaining steamers. *Geneva Cross* left South Wharf on 21 February 1933, the *Maltese Cross* on 28 February and the *Red Cross* on 6 March for mooring at Erith, after being disinfected and certified as such by the Port Sanitary Authority. The first two proceeded under their own steam and the *Red Cross* in tow as instructed by the Chief Engineer, signed E.G. Giblin.

APPENDIX 3

Treatment

From *Enquire within upon Everything* 1884: To prevent pitting after smallpox: spread a sheet of thin leather with the ointment of ammoniacum with mercury, and cut out a place for the mouth, eyes and nostrils. Allow to remain for three days for the distinct kind and four days for the runny variety. Apply before the spots fill with matter – or – touch every pustule, or poc, on the face or bosom with a camel-hair pencil dipped in a weak solution of lunar caustic (nitrate of silver) – or – smear the whole surface of the body after the eruption is fairly out with bacon fat.

From the notes of patients on the Hospital Ships:
To the face: 1:200 formalin, or 1:2000 mercuric chloride, or cover with collodion and strip off after three days.

To the eyes: 1:5000 mercuric chloride or 1:2000 iodoform (to eye lids) or silver nitrate drops and atropine ointment.

Limbs: Rest by splinting and protect by wrapping in cottonwool and/or darkened room (red light treatment).

Throat and Lungs: Permanganate of Potash gargle, inhalation of terebene, glycerine of borax.

Sedatives: Sulphonal, Paraldehyde, Nepenthe

Stimulants: Injections of strychnine, brandy, or aether and brandy
Oral: Brandy and champagne 1 ounce every hour, increased to 2 ounces half hourly but omit brandy. Quinine sulphate.

In extremis: Peptonized milk and tea enema 6 hourly.

BIBLIOGRAPHY

Alerte! *Paris Match* Jan 1962 p61.
Ayers, G.M. *England's First State Hospitals,* Wellcome 1961.
British Medical Journal, Sep 1905.
Buchanan, G.S. *Smallpox in the Orsett Union,* Brit. Med. J. 1903 p618.
Burne, C.S. *Shropshire Folklore,* Trubner & Co 1883.
Burne, J.C. *The Grounds of Joyce Green Hospital, The Garden* Nov 1980.
Chaplin, C. *My Autobiography,* Penguin Books 1964.
Enquire Within upon Everything, Houlston & Sons 1884.
Guinness Book of Names, 1974.
Harker, S. *The Book of Gravesham,* Barracuda Books 1979.
Health Exhibition Lit, Clowes, London 1884.
Keyes, S.K. *Dartford Historical Notes,* Perry Son & Lack 1933 & 1938.
Lancet, Nov. 1904 p1302.
Letter Book of the Hospital Ships, 1895–1901.
Letter Book of the River Hospitals, 1907–1913.
Marsden, J.P. Bulletin of Hygiene, Oct 1949.
Price, J.A. *London's Last Horse Tramway,* J. Transport History, May 1962.
Metropolitan Asylums Board, *Minutes 1881–1930.*
Registers of Staff of Ships & River Hospitals, 1892–1914.
Report Books of Matron River Hospitals, 1914–1933.
Reports of the Medical Superintendent of the Hospital Ships, 1895–1902.
Reports of the Medical Superintendent of the River Hospitals, 1902–1947.
Reports of the Superintendent of the River Ambulances, 1885–1933.
Ricketts, T.F. & Byles, J.B. *Red Light Treatment of Smallpox,* Lancet 1904 ii 287 & 816.
Ricketts, T.F., *The Diagnosis of Smallpox,* Cassell & Co 1908.
Rowles, W., *Built at Brimscombe Port,* Waterways World 1978.
Savage, J., *Brimscombe,* Gloucestershire Life Aug. 1973.
Second Report of the Royal Commission on Vaccination, HMSO 1890.
Thurston, G. *The Great Thames Disaster,* Allen & Unwin 1965.
Tyler, J.A. *A History of Joyce Green Aerodrome 1911–1919.*
Wallenberg, J.K. *The Place-Names of Kent,* Uppsala 1934.
Wallenberg, J.K. *Kentish Place-Names,* Uppsala 1934.
Woodham-Smith, C. *Florence Nightingale,* Constable 1951.

KEY TO CAPTION CREDITS

WP	Woods and Porter	SG	Dr Spence Galbraith
DL	Dartford Division,	TFR	Dr T.F. Ricketts
	Kent County Library	NMM	National Maritime Museum
SB	Sheila Blackman	JT	John A. Tyler
A	Author	DA	Darenth Asylum Archives

All others come from the Joyce Green Hospital Archives

INDEX

ENDPAPERS — FRONT: Map of MAB institutions, c1900. BACK: Plan of Ambulance Steamer *Red Cross*, 1883.

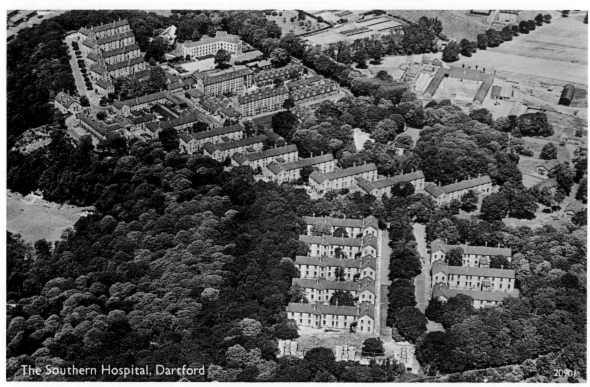

Aerial View of the Southern Hospital. The Darenth Asylum cemetery is top centre.

SUBSCRIBERS

Presentation Copies

1 Dartford Borough Council
2 Dartford Library
3 Kent County Council
4 Dartford & Gravesham Health Authority
5 District Health Authority Library, Joyce Green
6 The World Health Authority, Geneva
7 Rt Hon the Lord Irving of Dartford DL

8
9 Dr & Mrs John Burne
10 Roger Burne MB BS
11 Margaret Pichler
12 Christopher Burne
13 Helen Hicks
14 Clive & Carolyn Birch
15 Christoph Bull
16 Ken Jarvis
17 Pat Stevens
18 J. French
19 Dr H.D. Cheetham
20 Mr & Mrs B.V. Wiffen
21
22 Adrian Herbert
23 Mrs K.M. Whitehead
24 Robert J. Dunn MP
25 Dartford Borough Museum
26 P.W. Boreham
27 Mr & Mrs D. Phillips
28 Frank James Sayers
29 Bryan D.F. Clarke
30 C. Arnold
31 Herbert Dixon
32 G.A. Cramp
33 Gordon & Penny Martin
34 K. Chamberlain
35 Mrs B.E. Bacon
36 H.R. Lambert
37 Neil R. Langridge
38 Ian Rogers
39 Robert L. Eastleigh
40 Mary Hirschfeld
41 Kathryn Mulhall
42 Mrs H. Gambleton
43 Mrs E.A. Jenkins
44 A.F. & B.A. Robinson
45 Mrs S. Beadle
46 Terry Moyle
47 Richard Andersen Holdstock
48 Mrs Joyce Rose
49 P. Holmes
50 Ken Russell
51 Kieran Russell
52 M. Parry
53 Jean & Michael Le'Mon
54 Peter John Pratt
55 Mr & Mrs M.S. Renno
56 Mrs Jeannette M.H. Carter
57 Mrs Carole E. Pomfret
58 M.J.S. Smith
59 Trevor Knowles
60 L.C.W. Lawler
61 Maurice Saunders
62 Arthur Rutt
63 Mrs A. Evans
64 Terry & Sylvia Dabner
65 Olive M. Gibson
66 Mrs D. Hogan
67 Mrs G. Joyce
68 Mrs Joan P.A. Kelly
69 John Cassell
70 Public Relations Office, Dartford Borough Council
71 Mrs F.M. Roberts
72 Mrs J.M. King
73 R.J. Johnson

74
75 Mrs J. Spice
76 Mrs B. Mayell
77 Ian J.W. Reid
78 Mary M. Moore
79 Charles & Marion Heather
80 Mr & Mrs Norman F. Mills
81 R. Fincham
82 Miss E.D. Norgrove
83 R.J. Barnes
84 Mrs Joyce Wise
85 N.D. Allan
86 Vanessa & Glyn Smitherman
87 Valerie J. White
88 A. Andrew Gibbs
89 G.L. Bailey
90 Wendy & Derek Parsons
91 Drs Vibha & Amitabh Mohan
92 Donald & Georgina Look
93 E.G. Wagland
94 G.S. Moore
95 P. McLean
96 Mrs Jennifer Davies
97 M. Campbell
98 Mrs R. Bird
99 H. Jarman
100
101 Mrs R. Bird
102 Mrs J. Wallis
103 Miss N. Griffiths
104 Mrs Anne Knowles
105 Andrew Smith
106 Mrs P.P.M. Hudson
107 J.W. Downes
108 W.K. Gould
109 Mr & Mrs R. Aish
110 H.F. Weston
111 Mrs M.A. Wright
112 Mrs D.M. Moore
113 G.S. Hudson-Peacock
114 Doris Forsdyke
115 Mrs Joan M. Desforges
116 David Desforges
117 Marjorie Brown
118 G.A.N. Robinson
119 Peter Bryan
120 D.H. Turner
121 R.C. Dunham
122 G.C. Gray
123 Mrs B.M. Gray
124 F. Chatfield
125 Mrs Eileen Watson
126 Mr & Mrs D.J. Winch
127 J. Roe

128 Geoffrey James Torry
129 Dr John H. Hudson
130 Dr G.B. Stratton
131 Chris Burne
132 Miss K. Cousins
133 Audrey & Ron Phillips
134 Mrs P.J. Chapman
135 Mrs R.M. Grix
136 Ms K.L. Sargeant
137 Mrs Laura J. Lincoln
138 Dartford Historical & Antiquarian Society
139 I.F. Smith
140 Mrs M. Perkins
141 L.F. Dunn
142 Mrs T.A. Bourne
143 Mrs S.M. Franklin
144 Miss O. Barnaby
145 C.A. & J. Ovenden
146 Miss B. Leach
147 Paul Homer
148 D. Barker
149 Mrs D.A. Gregory
150 Dr & Mrs Burne
151 Mrs Drew
152 Jane Burne
153 Richard Burne
154 Mrs J.L. Beven
155 Dr Spence Galbraith
156 Charles Mulhall
157 Gary Jenkins
158 The Library,
160 Joyce Green Hospital
161 Helena Scott
162 Elsie K. Evans
163 Alan Hull
164 Mrs V. Bishop
165 Mrs A.E. Jarrett
166 A.K. Brown
167 D.V. Samson
168 J.M. Heathfield
169 Jan Clarke
170 Dartford Central
190 Library
191 Mrs Beryl Moorehead
192 Mrs East
193 Mrs Godfrey
194 Mrs R.G. Shakespeare
195 W.G. Williams
196 K.G. Tuffrey
197 Mrs I.D. Mucci
198 Mr & Mrs W. Jenkins
199 Beryl & Derrick Taylor
200 G.R. Howard
201 Janet Vallins
202 Ann Fletcher
203 M. Hodgson

204 Margaret Pichler
205 Nicole Pichler
206 David Pichler
207 Mrs Wilkins
208 F.J. Clarke
209 Derek Thorogood
210 Mrs R. Hodge
211 H.C. Potterton
212 J.R. Summers
213 Miss Glenda Thomas
214 G.H. Maytum
215 Mrs B. Medhurst
216 Mrs B. Smith
217 Mrs E. Andrew
218 A. Openshaw
219 Mrs I.V. Ball
220 Mrs Pauline Wood
221 Mrs Maureen Owen
222 W.F. Wood
223 A. West
224 D.G. Robinson
225 M.J. Barlow
226 Mrs Joy Gowland
227 D.J.C. & Mrs G.C. Simpson
228 Mr & Mrs T. Scarth
229 Mrs S. Smith
230 Mrs I. Wells
231 Mrs J.C. Thomas
232 Miss E.M. Couzins
233 Dr M. Coughlan
234 Kent County Library,
238 Gravesend/Northfleet Group
239 Mr & Mrs E.G. Good
240
241 F. Warren
242 Graham & Veronica Titcombe
243 John Kierans
244 Miss E.R.L. Thomas
245 Miss D.M. Wells
246 Deryck Jones
247 Jean & Ted Foreman
248 J.G. May
249 George Ballard
250 Mrs M. Warby
251 P. Dean
252 Mrs S.M. Durrant
253 R.E. Harris
254 T. Page
255 P.M. Simnor
256 J. Williams
257 B.J. Simnor
258 Mr & Mrs P. Cavanagh
259 Miss Joyce E. Parker
260 Mrs F.M. Roberts
261 Mrs Joan Inglis
262 D.A. Summers
263 W.G. Lewis
264 M. Nash
265 R. Saunders
266 E.H. Rainer
267 E.A. Anderson
268 C.G. Young
269 Mrs B. Acott
270 Mr & Mrs A. Boyling
271 R.W.J. Neville
272 Miss Margaret E. Lewis
273 Roy A. Edwards
274 Dr J.A. Reader
275 Mrs D.H. Gregory

276 Mrs E.E. Mitchell
277 Miss J. Pollard
278 Mrs J. Harker
279 Mrs Penny Turvey
280 David A. Goodchild
281 N.F. Hall
282 R. Peacock
283 R. Smith
284 B.J. Faint
285 A. Freeman
286 Mrs Phillipa Johnston
287 E.W. Johnston
288 Mrs C. Collin
289 Mrs C. Whitebread
290 R.M. Pain
291 K. Bennett
292 Miss E.J. Barnes
293 Mrs K.M. Rolfe
294 Dr G.B. Stratton
295 J.A.E. Watts
296 Mr & Mrs Alan
    Cheeseman
297 K.J.M. Walter
298 R.K. Walter
299 J.F. Walter
300 C.L. Rose
301 Miss P. Moore
302 Oliver Moore
303 D.J.P. Hurley
304 Mrs Ann Clubb
305 Mrs H. Oaten
306 Mrs J.M. Byrne
307 Mrs M.E. Jowett
308 Martin Mason JP
309 Mr & Mrs David J.
    Atkins
310 Mrs B.J. Smith
311 Ronald Carter
312 Mrs R.M. Dunmall
313 Mrs I. Tait
314 David Phillips
315 J.C. Phillips
316 Mervyn Ross Jones
317 Mrs G.J. Phillips
318 Garry Watkins
319 D.J. Powley
320 Herbert J.W.
    Ticehurst
321 Mr & Mrs F.W.
    Matthews
322 P.J. Chapman
323 Mrs S.E. Kipps
324 A.R. Marchant
325 Michael R.
    Thompson
326 Mrs A. Rogan
327 Ruth Cheeseman
328 Patience Burne
329 Kathleen Mackney
330 V.H. Eustace
331 Wellcome Unit for
    the History of
    Medicine
332 P.L. Newman
333 P.G. Fisher
334 M.J.G. Southern
335 C.H. Maytum
336 Dr M. Hemmings
337 Miss K.M. Roome
338 Carol Ballard
339 Mrs M.V. Wilmot
340 Mrs Pauline Taft
341 Peter Draper
342 Cllr D.H.W. Turner

343 Michael G. Bruce
344 Mrs P.M. Cartwright
345 Dr N.M. Mann
346 A. Nicholson
347 Frank Hughes
348 Mrs Arlene E. Rayner
349 E.J.R Miller
350 J.H. Sandeford
351 Miss E.M. Rees CBE
352 Fay Reeve
353 A. Tickner
354 E.A.F. Milner
355 Rev C.J.S. Burne
356 Mr & Mrs C.M.
    Hewett
357 Dr N.L. Short
358 P.W. Stone
359 Richard Campbell
360 Miss M. Long
361
362 Dr A.F. Crick
363 D.B. Welbourn
364 Derek Moody
365 John A. Butler
366 Y. Wakefield
367 Miss Thelma Taylor
368 J. McQuillan
369 Mrs P.A. Salama
370 Mrs Teresa Johnson
371 Mrs Elizabeth
    Rampling
372 Mrs Angela Hawkins
373 Margaret Dunn
374 James A. Ryan
375 C.G. Lane
376 Mr & Mrs W.T. Dann
377 Mr & Mrs L. Upsher
378 J.H. Evans
379 Raymond Kitching
380 Joan M. Green
381 Thomas Dell
382 Miss Patricia
    Northcott
383 Robert J. Wilson
384 J. M. Blacklock
385 Dr M. Worboys
386 M.L. Fergusson
387
388 Gillingham Library
389 B.E. Sleigh
390 Rear Admiral P.N.
    Marsden
391 C.P. Braithwaite
392 National Maritime
    Museum Library
393 Alan Wild
394 Mrs M.R. Newton
395 W. Porter
396 Mrs J. Hayes
397 Miss Lisa Burns
398 Mrs M. Millar
399 J. Blundell
400 Mrs M. Bloxham
401 G.C. Mitchell
402 Dartford Hospital
    School
403
404 K.P. Challinger
405 Anthony Charles
    Clark
406 Dr L.M. Elliott
407 Doreen R.
    Meddemmen
408 W.L. Roose

409 Mrs S.P. Wells
410 Mrs P.E. Hoskins
411 Miss J.R. Wood
412 Mrs J. Farrell
413 Mrs W.I. Ratcliffe
414 Mrs F. Fisk
415 B.D. Marriott
416 G.F. Farr
417 S.J.R. Wilson
418 R.J. Elgie
419 J. Wright
420 G.A. Gregory
421 Baily & Goff
422 Ronald F.
    Mace FCCA
423 A.B. Smith
424 Mrs Marilyn Moat
425 Daphne Roberts
426 Miss E.R. Duff
427 Henry John
    Rogers MBE
428 Ian M. Reader
429 Stanley John Stringer
430 Mrs J.M. Jones
431 Mrs M.G. Healey
432 Mrs Gwen Phillips
433 Gladys J. Palmer
434 E.L. Sparshott
435 Colin P. Allsop
436 Moira A. Chandler
437 James S. Oddy
438 Marion Tofts
439 Miss E.M. Vinall
440 F.J. White
441 Thomas A.
    Thompson
442 Josephine
    Birchenough
443 R.H. Wells
444 R.H. Jetts
445 Simon E. Price
446 B.R. Whitehead
447 Roy Turley
448 R.G. Wells
449 W. Ward
450 Mr & Mrs S.G.
    Willson
451 Mrs E. Sparks
452 Mr & Mrs P.F.
    Winton
453 Gerald Whiting
454 R. White
455 B.G. Port
456 Michael Wiffen
457 K.T. Ray
458 Mrs J. Taylor
459 Mrs V.L. Pike
460 Mr & Mrs D.L. Page
461 Mr & Mrs R.
    Whymark
462 Lynne Prescott
463 Beryl Bingham
464 Frederick A. Langley
465 Miss A. Viner
466 Mrs Daphne Studd
467 Mrs P.H. Alford
468 Graham Groves
469 C. Bradbury
470 Mrs P. Thompson
471 Dr N.S. Galbraith
472 Nada Hammond
473 Bernard Crowhurst
474 Barbara & David
    Walden

475 Mrs P.A. Wakefield
476 G.M. Osmotherly
477 Doris Simmons
478 David Pearson
479 Dr P.A. Gardner
480 K. Bridge
481 Darryl F. Royce
482 Dr Roger Peppiatt
483 Dr P.W. Pitt
484 Dr E.J. Mitchell
485 Angela King
486 A. Elliott
487 S. Barber
488 D.S.L. Hermitage
489 B. Gunther
490 M. Fraser
491 Dr D. Wise
492 P.M. Thompson FRCS
493 W.F. Jaycocks
494 The Lady Murray of
    Gravesend
495 J.D. Wakeling
496 J.F. Sheehan
497 K.P. Goldman
498 Alan John Sale
499 Dartford Grammar
    School for Girls
500 Dr E. Gancz
501 C.R. Green
502 Dr Mary Hann
503
504 E.D. Skidmore OBE
505 Dr J.M. Forsythe
506 Mr & Mrs J.C.
    Strachan
507 Miss G.E. Crowhurst
508 North West Kent
    Family History
    Society (Dartford &
    District Branch)
509 A.E. Hendry
510 Doreen Deakin
511 Dr P.C. Farrant
512 Mrs S. Fenton
513 Dinah C.M. Brown
514 Margaret Baker
515 Peter F. Bates
516 Keith F. Blacker
517 D.B. Tunstill
518 Mrs A. Papworth
519 R.H. Phillpott
520 Robert Malsem
521 Dartford &
    Gravesham
    Community Health
    Council
522 Maureen Nowell
523 Philip Basford
524 Miss E.M. Tookey
525 Miss Melba Williams
526 Frances Sherlock
527 Joyce Moon
528 V.E. Andrews
529 R.T. Hattrill
530 G.I. Small
531 Mr & Mrs Dow
532 Mr & Mrs Pell
533 Mr & Mrs J. L. Topping
534 Mrs S. Bradley
535 Mrs E.F.S. Bradshaw
536 W.H. Freeman
537 M.W. Hogan

Remaining names unlisted

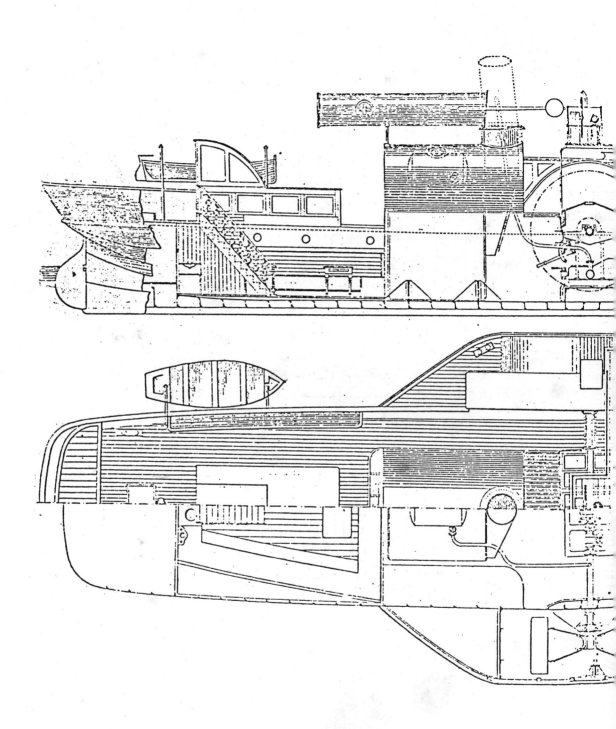